The 5 Most
Dangerous Words
In The
English Language:

MAYBE
IT
WILL
GO
AWAY!

*"Understand you but waste time
unless you go beyond what you have learned
to what is yet to learn."*

A Gift of Peace,
Course In Miracles

Awaken the Healer Within

PRIME
BOOKS
INCORPORATED

**Cataloguing in Publication Data
Main entry under title:**

**Hansen, Mark Victor
Awaken the healer within**

ISBN 1-895250-56-0

1. Mental healing. 2. Mind and body. I. Title.

RZ400.H35 1992   615.8'51   C92-093896-5

OTABIND

Publisher's Note

Otabind (Ota-bind). This book has been bound using the patented Otabind process. You can open this book at any page, gently run your finger down the spine, and the pages will lie flat.

**Printed in Canada
Cover design by ACP Associates, Markham, Ontario**

**Prime Books Incorporated
211 Consumers Road, Suite 201
Willowdale, Ontario M2J 4G8
Phone (416) 502-1949 Fax (416) 502-1953**

PRIME
BOOKS
INCORPORATED

Table of Contents

*"You will be made whole
As you make whole."*
A Gift of Peace,
Course In Miracles

This book is dedicated to all the people who have contributed to sound health throughout the centuries, to all the people who endeavor to carry that message forward, and to all those who profit from their advice.

> *"Many receive advice,*
> *only the wise profit from it."*
>
> Syrus

Introduction
by
Mark Victor Hansen

You have healing power. We all do. If you want to release more healing power, this book is for you.

Give yourself permission to really awaken the healing power within you. You will be glad you did; others will thank you in their prayers for sourcing and serving them with your vast healing powers.

Every writer of this book is a close, personal friend. They individually and collectively know their stuff. They have the healing juices powering through their heads, hearts, hands, mouths, and now through the printed word. This book will inspire you to new levels of awakening. As you read it, you will keep saying 'aha'; 'Aha', as glimpses of enlightenment, flash onto the screen of your mind's eye. Your perspectives will be enlarged, enhanced, and improved as the thoughts in this delicious book caress your mind. The authors are my great friends. More importantly, each is a consummate, competent professional whom I trust and depend on, who is always of positive mental attitude, resonating in confidence, and perpetually going the extra mile for whomever they are serving. I love, respect and admire the authors of this book. Their insights will stimulate, amuse, and provoke you to rethink and improve your life and lifestyle.

I recommend you read this book with multiple-colored highlighters. You will want to return again and again to these illuminating insights that are destined to make your life, and the lives of those you meet, infinitely better. Also, write notes in the margin. My dear friends have "wowed" me on every page. I am so thankful they agreed to share their deep and profound insights and wisdom with love and kindness. Each is a marvelous human being, a great and inspiring teacher and delightful story-teller.

Their ideas will live positively and usefully in your mind long after you set down this book. Keep it handy—you will be reading a paragraph here and there to your friends in need. Perhaps you will consider an investment in a second copy so you can lend it to others whom you love and for whom you want the absolute best.

Healing is a science. Healing is a learnable, duplicative and transferable process. As you read, these authors will tell you their healing story. Whatever you need or want to heal will be revealed herein. Healing is revealing. These individuals each have a cornucopia of experience. Their story is transparent, and is your story. By the book's end, you will rewrite your own story and give it a happy, joyous, blissful new ending. Congratulations on reading a book which will benefit you personally, professionally, and familially.

This book tells what to heal, how to heal it, and why to heal it. My colleagues didn't write a home run of a book, they wrote a grand slam hit. Throughout my copy of this book, I kept writing "YES!" in the margin as their thinking verified and confirmed what I had suspected. Likewise, I suspect you too will write in your book "YES!", and be thankful it is so.

Mark Victor Hansen, a popular speaker to health professionals' conferences worldwide, appreciates your comments. You may reach him by writing to Mark Victor Hansen & Associates, 711 West 17th Street, Suite D-2, Costa Mesa, California 92627, or by telephoning (714) 759-9304.

DR. MICHAEL BILLAUER
AND
MADONNA BILLAUER, M.A.

Madonna and Michael Billauer, a husband and wife team, are recognized authorities on the subjects of health, fitness, and exercise/ movement. Sought after lecturers, consultants, and contributors in their respective fields, they have presented at universities, hospitals, healing centers, chiropractic conferences, and motivational seminars. Their work has taken them around the world to many countries including China, Russia, Korea, Mexico, and Cuba.

Articles written by Michael have been printed in the Santa Monica Evening Outlook, Volleyball Monthly magazine, plus American Fitness Quarterly, and he has spoken on KABC-Talk radio in Los Angeles.

Articles concerning Madonna have appeared in the Los Angeles Times, Daily News, Variety, and L.A. Weekly. She has consulted for video and motion pictures. For 11 years, she taught numerous dance and fitness courses in UCLA and also lectured at the University Medical School, Mark Taper Center For Health Enhancement and Assilimar.

The purpose of this team is to turn on life in each person by increasing one's awareness of the "whole" body thereby awakening the healer within, through chiropractic and movement.

They are available to speak on various health, fitness, exercise/movement, and motivational related subjects and can be contacted by writing Billauer Chiropractic, 3223 Washington Boulevard, Marina del Rey, California 90292. Michael can also be reached by telephoning (310) 306-1983 where he maintains his busy chiropractic practice and Madonna, who teaches at UCLA and Santa Monica Hospital, can be reached at (310) 471-5232.

1 THE TRINITY OF HEALTH

What Is The Trinity Of Health?

The Trinity is our divine design. We are the manifestation of the universal intelligence here on earth: all perfect; all natural; for our purpose; 100% of the time. The three sides of our divine design as we view it are the mental, physical, and spiritual.

In chiropractic, we believe that innate intelligence is *the doctor*, the healer within—our job is to balance these three components of the whole, so that the life force can come through from above—down—inside us and out.

According to DeGiacomo, on the larger scale, a study of any of the myriad examples of nature shows a delicate balance in the harmonious inter-relationship of these component parts. This harmonious balance is further evidence of an organization so vast and complex as to stagger the imagination. If even one part of the balance of nature is disturbed, the entire structure is weakened.

Our immediate and more intimate structure is the body in which we live. The chiropractor helps and views it from three aspects: the physical, which is structural or mechanical; the mental, which is emotional or spiritual; and, the chemical, which is nutritional or hormonal.

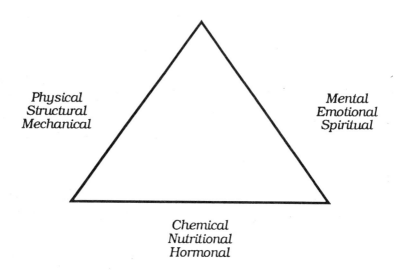

Physical
Structural
Mechanical

Mental
Emotional
Spiritual

Chemical
Nutritional
Hormonal

The living body is a complex phenomenon. Balancing it is a lifelong endeavour of adaptations. The newborn infant contains within it everything it will ever need throughout life, with the exception of food and oxygen. The power that created the baby's body is always naturally available *within* to heal the body throughout its lifetime. This is called *The Healer Within*.

What is Health?

Health is harmony: the maximum state of organization in which every cell is harmoniously functioning to fulfil its purpose for the benefit of the entire organism. This is a state of supreme order. Health is also wholeness, in which all parts of the body are functioning at 100% expression of intelligence through matter (structure) all the time. When the trinity is perfect, health is perfect.

When this trinity is out of balance, disharmony begins, malfunctions occur, and eventually symptoms develop.

What are Symptoms?

Symptoms are the body's indicators of loss of function. This could be compared to the red oil light on the dashboard of an automobile, indicating abnormal function. The healer within cringes if substances are taken to alleviate the symptoms without addressing the real cause of the problem. This is like painting the oil light so it won't be seen. The healer within knows it is only a mask or cover-up that allows the condition to further degenerate, only without conscious awareness. The healer within wants to *find* the cause of the warning signal and *correct* the problem so that the body may return to functioning at 100% efficiency.

In this chapter, we will look at the three components: the physical, mental, and chemical. We will provide the characteristics of imbalance, examinations to determine if imbalance exists, exercises, and a plan for *Finding the Balance*.

PART I
PHYSICAL-STRUCTURAL-MECHANICAL

In chiropractic, we say that structure determines function. If the structure is altered, the function is altered. Muscles are the levers of the body which attach to the bony structures in order to move the body. If the structure is torqued out of position, the muscles or levers will be pulled in skewed directions causing excessive torque and stress to the joints of the body. This results in joint problems such as inflammation, and over the long term, degeneration.

More importantly, the nervous system, composed of the brain, spinal cord and nerves, is protected by the vertebral column. The nervous system carries the life force—innate intelligence or universal intelligence, the healer within, spirit, or God if you will—to every tissue cell in the body, so that it may function at 100% of its potential. If the structure of the vertebral column is disturbed by trauma, or lack of exercise, or too much exercise, or poor posture, etc., this life force can be blocked by a pinched nerve, for example. Therefore, the tissue cells do not receive complete mental messages and do not function at 100% potential. This altered structure results in altered function of the tissue cells, organs, muscles, and the body as a whole. The healer within is disturbed and *dis-ease* begins. At this stage, the dis-ease process is without symptoms (warnings) and we function abnormally, but unknowingly. When symptoms first appear, we erroneously conclude that the problem has just begun, when in actuality it has been present for some time.

An example of the healer within us can be seen in a situation we have all faced many times in our lives, yet take for granted.   A cut in our skin in time heals up *by itself.* This healing process is controlled by the brain, through the nervous system and the particular nerve to the area of the skin where the cut is located. The nervous system senses the lesion, then mobilizes and coordinates the chemical reactions necessary to heal the wound. This all takes place without any conscious effort. Yet, if the nerve that senses the area of the skin where the lesion occurred were to be severed, the healing process would never occur and the lesion would last indefinitely.

A common example of symptoms appearing many years after the problem begins is a typical one where a patient suddenly recognizes a stiff neck. The patient's history reveals an automobile accident fifteen years prior, in which there was only minor stiffness for one week. Since that time, there have been no symptoms. The X-rays taken at this time reveal signs of degeneration (arthritis) of the bones in the neck, a process that evolved over fifteen years with no symptoms, until now.

In eleven years of clinical practice, I have seen thousands of cases in which structural malpositions—vertebral subluxations—have interfered with the function of the nervous system and blocked the *healer within* from doing its job. Chiropractic is best known for its results with musculoskeletal disorders, such as lower back pain, neck pain, and headaches. However, when nerve pressure is relieved, dramatic results often occur, affecting all areas of the body. Some of the other conditions which have responded favorably include: ear infections, colic, asthma, hearing and vision loss, elbow and knee problems, dizziness, constipation, menstrual problems, and many others.

Case History: Nicholas was a seven-year old asthmatic boy who took oral medication and used an inhaler. He loved to play soccer, but could not run the length of the field without using his inhaler. He was found to have several pinched nerves in his upper back which related to his lung apparatus, and within two months of beginning chiropractic care, the pinched nerves were freed, the healer within went to work, and he no longer suffered from asthma.

Most people are motivated to begin care after the symptoms appear. If care is given immediately, the length of time of correction can be minimized.

Spinal correction is dependent on the age, occupation, physical condition, severity of the problem, and the length of time the problem has existed. In a child, correction can usually be accomplished in a relatively short time (from 1-2 weeks to 1-2 months). In an elderly person, where the condition has been present for many years and spinal degeneration has occurred, complete correction may not be possible. In such cases, treatment may take one to two years for maximum stabilization, followed by periodic care to maintain this stability.

To keep the healer within awake, frequent, periodic check-ups of the condition of the spine are most effective as they allow for early discovery and correction of a spinal problem.

The transformation of a physical body is a primary benefit of chiropractic. We have found that combining chiropractic with exercise helps integrate the greater cognitive (mental thought) and emotional transformation.

All three facets are important for optimal health. They all work synergistically, where divine grace and human activity cooperate in the work of regeneration. In chiropractic and the fitness field, we have realized that exercise is an essential action or element in the matrix of health, for with it come changes in behavior and physiology that can directly enhance a person's experience.

In my eleven years of teaching at the University, I have seen thousands of individuals awaken the healer within through exercise. An effective exercise/movement program helped in:

- enhancing muscular stability, balance, and strength;

- strengthening the abdominal muscles that support the back, improve posture, and efficiency of structure;

- improving circulation, stamina, and productivity;

- increasing metabolism and efficiency of food usage;

- easing gastrointestinal disorder and constipation;

- balancing hormonally and stress-induced mood swings;

- producing the body's natural pain killer *endorphins*;

- producing better reasoning ability and better reaction time;

- extending the life span, which has been proven in many studies; and

- giving one access to the body to experience the grace of life and to know oneself, which can be a joyous and important experience.

It has been my fortunate experience to have seen that individuals with depression, diabetes, asthma, high cholesterol, high blood pressure, bursitis, and strokes were aided by exercise and were most often allowed to reduce or eliminate, with a doctor's consent, the dosage of required medication.

The basic formula for an effective exercise program is to increase one's core temperature, or body heat, two times a day or to perform a cardiovascular activity for 15 to 20 minutes, three times per week, or every other day.

Now, finding a balance with an exercise (movement) program is a process. It is best to start easily, and gradually add more time and/or intensity, while staying comfortable. As you feel more fit, the benefits will show and your lifestyle will have been changed for the betterment of your whole self.

Do note that when you have not done enough exercise, stress builds up and becomes pent up energy causing muscles to tighten and eventually spasm. When you have done too much exercise, you can strain yourself; lactic acid builds up in the muscles, and they become restrictively sore. Find the balance between the two.

There are many exhilarating, refreshing, and centering choices of exercise and movement activities that are effective and can be enjoyable:

- increasing your amount of housework;

- choosing to stand more than sit;

- starting to walk more;

- climbing stairs;

- running;

- swimming;

- Tai Chi;

- yoga;

- dance;

- sports (e.g. basketball, tennis, skiing);

- exercise classes and equipment;

- even visualizing a vigorous activity.

Taking charge of your physical activity will reward you with a sense of satisfaction and confidence, and will add self-direction to your lifestyle and character.

I have noticed that exercise is a cathartic experience and can become a form of meditation. The rhythm of repetitive movements can be similar to a mantra.

Through exercise/movement, healing will occur on many levels, and each interaction, if done carefully, will promote a balance.

When exercising, it is possible to achieve a trance state where your inner voice gives you direction, confidence, and the condition to take action on what is most important in your life.

Exercise, or any human movement activity, is the most powerful tool for fusing your body, mind, and soul (spirit) connection. It enhances the fusing of the logical with the intuitive, the analytical perceptions with the sensual perceptions, and a marriage of wholistic understanding with step-by-step thinking. It is *the* discipline which within itself, deals with the basic understanding of human experience and our conceptualization.

PART II
CHEMICAL-NUTRITIONAL-HORMONAL

The second component of the triad is the chemical, nutritional, hormonal side. The body is a finely balanced chemical system with hundreds of thousands of chemical reactions taking place every second. When one thinks of chemicals, the first thing that may come to mind is industry. In fact, we too are made up of many different and incompatible chemicals.

In our modern age, we have learned of the dangers of industrial toxic waste in the air we breathe, the water we drink, and the food we eat. We have become more environmentally aware, yet the pollution around us is affecting us more than is commonly known.

Many of us have the attitude that it won't affect us. However, our innate intelligence knows differently. We must listen to our innate intelligence—the healer within—to protect our health. There is an awakening of more global concern, yet we must take responsibility on a personal level. It is easy to pollute ourselves also.

Are you aware of the chemicals you put in your body on a daily basis? Here is a sample test to determine if you are polluting yourself:

Chemical Test

		Yes	No
1.	Do you drink one or more cups of coffee a day?	❑	❑
2.	Do you smoke any cigarettes?	❑	❑
3.	Do you eat a candy bar to get through the day?	❑	❑
4.	Do you drink soda (diet or otherwise) to quench your thirst?	❑	❑
5.	Do you drink alcoholic beverages?	❑	❑
6.	Do you take aspirin or any other medications?	❑	❑
7.	Do you eat fast foods?	❑	❑
8.	Do you consume refined food products (such as those containing white sugar or white flour)?	❑	❑

9.   Do you consume products that   ❑ ❑
     contain preservatives, such as
     canned or boxed mixes?

10. Do you consume food with   ❑ ❑
     artificial color or flavorings?

If you have answered *yes* to any of the above
questions, then you are chemically polluting
yourself.

The purpose of this test is to make you aware
of what you are doing, and the purpose of this
section is to give you information and a plan to
modify your behavior. If you take a moment to
visualize yourself going inside your body and
residing in the intestine, you may then smell and
sense how we pollute ourselves. That which we
have eaten for lunch yesterday is today walking,
talking, flesh and blood. From a cheeseburger,
french fries, and a soda with refined white flour,
processed cheese, fats, sugar, and food coloring,
the body manufactures adrenaline, liver tissue,
brain tissue, and all the other multitude of
complex body structures.

A well-known expression is "garbage in,
garbage out". Think how disgusting it would be
to be bathed in garbage, yet this is what many of
us do with our poor dietary habits!

It can be very difficult to get away from all the food processing and fast food that surrounds us. We are constantly bombarded with advertisements through visual and auditory stimuli about the convenience and benefits of fast food or fast-acting drugs. This is done by huge corporations that make billions of dollars selling their goods. However, many of these products seriously inhibit normal bodily functions and disturb the healer within. The detrimental effects of these products are not well-known to the public because the companies either do not want us to know about them, or are not aware themselves. It is our individual responsibility to learn of the detrimental effects of any product we use, if they exist.

As you become more sensitive to your body, an awareness level surfaces which can distinguish the effects of different products on your body. For example, as you cut down on the amount of sugar you eat, you become more aware of its effect. You become aware of the quick burst of energy following its consumption, only then to experience extreme drowsiness, or the actual need for a nap. This results from the sugar product raising the blood sugar level within minutes of its consumption. The body then secretes insulin in a large quantity, to lower the high level of sugar in the blood, and this leads to a lower than normal level of blood sugar for a one-hour period. This lowered blood sugar induces the drowsiness. This process, repeated many times per day over many years, causes an imbalance in the system which can result in hypoglycaemia (low blood sugar), and some believe, eventually leads to diabetes.

Other examples exist, including the consumption of products high in fat content, cholesterol, and salt. Research has linked use of these products to many chronic, degenerative diseases such as cancer, heart disease, clogging and hardening of the arteries, arthritis, etc.

We must realize how the use of these products affects how we feel everyday, so that we can stop using them over long periods of time to prevent the manifestation of the above diseases in our bodies. If we are blind to the effects on a daily basis, we are shocked when we go to the doctor many years later and are told we have diabetes or heart disease, or even worse, cancer. These are diseases that take many years to manifest and so disturb the healer within. Recovery is made extremely difficult because the body has so deteriorated, that much of the strength to fight disease (the energy for the healer within) is lost.

Making changes in our old habits can be difficult or easy. It depends on each of us. The first requirement is the decision to make a change. Once that decision is made, the changes can be manifested. Those who find it difficult to change have not made a 100% decision that they want to change.

Since many of the habits are of a long-term nature, we recommend a more gradual approach to change as opposed to the sudden, instant type. While some people are strong-willed and can stop *cold turkey*, so to speak, for many, this is too difficult, and attempting to do it in this way will lead to frustration and failure.

With gradual change, self-confidence and the feeling of success can be built, and you begin to feel better; there is no feeling of total deprivation. For example, to decide to eliminate your use of one of the following items—coffee, cigarettes, sugar, chocolates, junk food, meat and drugs—determine how often they are consumed and ascertain how many years they have been consumed. Gradually eliminate use of these items over a period of from one to twelve months.

Write down your goal and place it where it can be seen easily, (bathroom mirror, dashboard, desk, phone area or refrigerator) at least twice a day. This will facilitate an easier gradient of change. A feeling of successful accomplishment will permit you to become appreciative of your naturally functioning body, so that you realize the benefits of your *health* when less use of the so-called *vice, sinful or poisonous* products are chosen. This will fuel your desire to stop using these products and help you to attain your goal.

Once your goal has been accomplished with one product, elimination of the rest of the products will be easier. A feeling of wellness and confidence will become very apparent and the healer within will wake up. In our view, this is the ultimate goal.

All of the aforementioned detrimental products are stresses to our body. As many of us know, stress affects our bodies, causing our muscles to tighten up and/or weaken. But many people are unaware of the internal effects of stress on the organs of the body. Stress causes the *stress gland* or adrenal glands of the body to secrete hormones. These hormones, in turn, affect the other organs of the body—the heart, lungs, stomach, small and large intestine, liver, and kidneys.

One single, stressful event will cause secretion of the adrenal hormones. When the event is over, the secretion stops, and after the effect of the hormones has been achieved, the body is returned to balance. If our bodies are constantly bombarded with stressful events and situations—job related, finance related, and family life related, compounded by the use of coffee, cigarettes, sugar, drugs, etc.—our adrenal glands are constantly overworked and eventually become fatigued.

At this stage, our body can no longer cope with stress, and we become *stressed out*, so to speak, and develop allergies which we may never have had before. We also become more susceptible to illness. Dysfunctions of some of the organs now begin to appear, such as ulcers, constipation, diarrhea, gas problems, indigestion, asthma, chest pain, etc. Development of these conditions leads many to take medications, whether they be non-prescription or prescription, not realizing that the conditions are merely symptoms and not the real problem.

The drugs become an added stress because they cover up or mask the symptom which is the body's warning signal. Thus, drugs make us unaware of what is happening to us. We think we are getting better (symptoms go away or are numbed) but in actuality, we are getting worse but don't realize it. Many of the drugs have side-effects which are more harmful than the original condition and add even more stress to your body and health.

The solution is to clean up your act, eliminating those products so that your body can cope with the stresses you can not control. Your body will balance itself, allowing the *healer within* to emerge.

PART III
MENTAL-EMOTIONAL-SPIRITUAL

For many, this component is the least understood. It cannot be seen, touched, or tasted. It is intangible, but it can be felt.

We all have an inner voice called *self-talk* that we hear constantly judging us. Is it optimistic or pessimistic? What does it say, "You can do it", or "you can't do it"? We have found that for most of us, the prevalent voice is the pessimistic side, the side that holds us back and can possibly talk us out of making our dreams come true. On the other hand, when we use the optimistic side, we realize that the greatest love of all is the love of one's self. The inner voice is then totally supportive, nurturing, and can help us grow, ultimately with no limitations.

The purpose of this section of the chapter is:

1)   to remove fear so that miracles of healing might happen;

2)   to enable the reader to preserve his health by switching to a lifestyle of right (healthy)

thinking in regard to himself and others; and

3)   to enable the patient to co-operate with the chosen health practitioner.

Faith in the alleviation of disease is a crucial factor, that knowingness that one will get better or is getting better. At the very least, faith enters into the selection of the best practitioner to handle the case. From this, we must realize, "As a man thinketh, so is he." You can think yourself sick or you can think yourself well. The choice is yours.   Furthermore, if proper thinking can influence healing, wrong thinking may have something to do with causing disease.

The fact that health can be worsened or improved by the mental attitude of the patient is recognized by every healer. Thinking has a lot to do with the recovery of the sick. But the possibility that thinking may have caused the sickness in the first place is rarely recognized.

Your job is to learn how to correct your thinking so as to bring about healing, and to learn how to avoid similar mistakes in the future.

Visualize Your Body Healing

Visualization is the use of mental pictures to assist your body in the healing process. Your subconscious responds strongly to pictures—this is an effective tool to help mobilize the healer within.

For example, you can build a mental image of an eraser or a vacuum cleaner eliminating, then cleaning up, diseased cells and tissues. There are several excellent books and tapes available to help you with visualization practice. We recommend books by Maxwell Maltz, Norman Cousins, and Louise Hay.

Use Positive Affirmations

Whether you are aware of it or not, you are talking to yourself all the time. *Choose* to make this positive self-talk. Say to yourself:

"I am in perfect, radiant health."
or
"I am well, I am well."

Make up your own affirmations. A study completed at Stanford University found that patients who used positive affirmations recovered more quickly than those who did not.

When we can get ourselves and our personal interests *out of the way* and just let God (or universal intelligence, or our life force) take over, we can be certain that the thoughts which appear under such circumstances originate within. We may receive direct guidance with regard to decisions, moves, and clear insight into complicated situations. In fact, many people who have developed the habit of meditating find that their lives become ordered by a power far above their own.

Meditation takes practice, but it pays tremendous dividends. There are many different ways to meditate. Find one that is comfortable for you.

It remains for the patient, himself, to direct his thinking, so that fear, doubt and worry are discarded. This will make the healer's work easier and recovery quicker. It may not be easy to acquire such control, but the will to get well is better based on something more reliable than the mere determination not to succumb to the sickness. An indomitable will has often proven to be the main factor in recovery. Yet, not all people have a strong enough will.

In *Think and Grow Rich*, Napoleon Hill says "Act as if you already have it." One way of accomplishing this state of mind is through gratitude for the things you already have, such as your life, family, friends, the healer within, and many more. Deep down, you feel that you are entitled to health, well-being, and the good things of life. Otherwise, there would be no sense in trying to attain them or regain them, if they seem to be lost. Act as if you already have what you want, such as health and vitality, and you will overcome those things that try to keep you from manifesting that which rightfully belongs to you.

In Conclusion

In conclusion, man has become too preoccupied with symptoms and does not truly appreciate the magnificence and capability of the healing power of the body, which is the grace of our divine design. By properly maintaining your structural alignment, keeping your body free from pollutants, and having a physically active lifestyle, plus realizing that a greater power and intelligence exists, you will successfully awaken the healer within. Think, visualize, and affirm, and you will manifest what you want.

We will try today to find
the source of healing,
which is in our minds ...
It is not farther from us than ourselves.
It is as near to us as our own thoughts;
so close it is impossible to lose.
We need but seek it, and it must be found.
                    A Gift of Peace,
                    Course In Miracles

TOMAS NANI

Tomas Nani is an author and professional speaker with over fifteen years of training in the various healing arts. In 1977, he took his first workshop on massage and fell in love with it immediately. He has studied with many of the top healers throughout the country and in this chapter he shares some of what he has learned about the importance of human touch in healing.

Tomas is also a highly successful business person. He is founder and President of Earthlite Massage Tables, Inc.

Since childhood, Tomas has always taken a keen interest in helping others. Becoming a licensed massage therapist in 1983 allowed him to merge his interest in healing with his desire to help others.

Sincere and with a loving heart, Tomas' passion is healing humanity by sharing the awareness of healing throughout the world. He is available for talks and workshops.

You may contact him by writing: Earthlite Massage Tables, Inc., 120 North Pacific Street, Suite L-7, San Marcos, CA 92069, or by telephoning him at (800) 872-0560.

2 | THE HEALING TOUCH

What is so important about touch anyway? What's all this fuss about fitness, wholistic health, and the harmful effects of stress? And what does it have to do with me?

Plenty, if you would like to lead a happy, and I emphasize happy, and healthy life. Most people believe themselves to be fairly relaxed and healthy, emotionally and physically. I am sad to say that in this fast-paced world of today, this is far from the truth; but take hope, there is a simple solution to counter the stress of modern life.

We, as a people, have forgotten what it is to be relaxed. We face pressures today that didn't exist one hundred years ago. Overstimulation by the media, the pressures to succeed, the breakdown in the family, and our rapidly changing culture all contribute to our sense of uneasiness. Life used to be simple, but now we've lost the simplicity and don't know what or whom to trust.

All of our time-saving inventions of the last century, which were supposed to create more leisure time for us, seem to have backfired. Today, everything is fast: fast food; fast cars; fast-tracked careers; we always seem to be running somewhere.

We go on vacation to relax and return more exhausted than when we left. Today's world goes at a faster pace than did the world of our parents, and the pace seems to get faster every year. The choice is ours—either we can decide to slow down and experience inner peace and healing, or our body and our mind will create an illness to slow us down. Almost everyone can remember a time when they themselves, or someone they know, were so pushed and stressed by life that they became sick, just so they could stop for a moment and have a break.

It is now believed that stress is a major contributing factor to almost every disease and illness. Stress, whether real or imagined, affects the body detrimentally. Some stress in life is healthy; what I'm concerned about are levels of stress that affect us in a negative way. Unfortunately, most people suffering the effects of stress are unaware that anything is wrong. This is because stress creeps in slowly, and the effects of stress are cumulative. We become accustomed to stress and soon forget what it is like to feel relaxed.

Do You Have Any Of These?

Some of the unhealthy effects of stress are:

- ❑ Ulcers
- ❑ Digestive Disorders
- ❑ High Blood Pressure
- ❑ Heart Disease
- ❑ Tense, Painful Muscles
- ❑ Headaches
- ❑ Insomnia
- ❑ Lowered Immune Resistance
- ❑ Depression
- ❑ Emotional Breakdown
- ❑ Skin Diseases
- ❑ Irritability or Anger
- ❑ Many Colds
- ❑ Sexual Difficulties
- ❑ Relationship Problems
- ❑ Memory Loss
- ❑ Anxiety and Fear

You may be asking, "What can I do to help myself, to relieve some of the negative effects of stress in my life?" Healing Touch, or Massage Therapy as it is now called, is one of the oldest healing therapies, dating back to at least three thousand years before Christ. And yet, it is one of the most misunderstood and unknown therapies available today.

Touch is a basic human need—as important as food and water. Every living creature craves and needs touch. Deprive a living being of touch and it dies. It has been shown in experiments that an infant monkey will choose touch over nourishment. Doctors are finding that premature babies have a much higher survival rate and develop more quickly if they are removed from their incubators and touched and stroked on a regular basis.

We live in a touch-deprived society. Our touch deprivation starts at birth. In our modern hospitals, infants are separated from their mothers. In our modern offices, mothers are separated from their infants as the number of double-income families continues to rise. This is in stark contrast to nature, where an infant chimpanzee is in almost constant, physical contact with its mother for the first four months of its life.

Touch is crucial to the proper growth and functioning of an infant's nervous system. Our children would grow up to be healthier and more emotionally balanced if we would only touch and hug them more. This is such an easy way to tap into your healing energies because as you hug or touch a child, your natural love and caring flow easily.

Touching is not part of our culture. There are so many taboo's against touching, mostly because of its association with sexuality.   In these times of increasing awareness of child molestation and sexual harassment, we are afraid to reach out and touch for fear it will be misinterpreted. Those of us who grew up without touching become adults who don't know how to touch or be touched. Through touch, we can communicate our love and caring. Sometimes when a child is hurt and crying, all they need is to be held, to be touched, and they feel better. An increasing number of enlightened psychologists and medical doctors are recommending four to six hugs a day as a way to maintain good health.

---

*Touch stimulates and relieves
the autonomic nervous system,
producing endorphins, the natural drug
for blocking pain and creating joy.*

What Massage Therapy Is

Massage Therapy is the perfect antidote for stress. Through massage, we can create a safe place to receive the love and caring we so desperately need. Massage sends a message to the body to slow down and relax. When you relax, your body begins its healing process. The first steps in any healing are slowing down and centering. Sometimes we get so wound up that it seems like we've forgotten how to unwind. Massage can help you tune in to your body and relax. With this relaxation comes a sense of wholeness and a harmony with yourself and your surroundings. In this still place created by massage, you are nurtured and renewed.

After a good massage, I feel like all the stresses and worries of my life have been erased and I get to start over from ground zero. I receive massage regularly, and sometimes I'm still surprised by how different I feel afterwards. Many people have remarked to me that after a massage, they feel centered and calm, and in touch with an inner wisdom they were not aware of before. Many businessmen use massage to boost their creativity and problem-solving abilities. When we get free from the tensions and stresses of life, our natural creativity and wisdom flows.

*"Only the person who is relaxed can create,
and to that mind ideas flow like lightning."*
Cicero

The Benefits of Massage

- ❏ Deep Relaxation
- ❏ Release of Tension
- ❏ Stress Reduction
- ❏ Increased Sense of Wellness
- ❏ Relief of Fatigue
- ❏ Increased Circulation
- ❏ Flushed and Cleansed Lymphatic System
- ❏ Improved Digestion
- ❏ Immune System Enhanced
- ❏ Lower Blood Pressure
- ❏ Relief from Tension-Related Headaches
- ❏ Relief of Muscle Pain and Soreness
- ❏ Increased Creativity
- ❏ Reduced Levels of Anxiety
- ❏ Satisfaction of Our Need for Care and Nurturance
- ❏ Relief of Pain of Arthritis
- ❏ Promotion of Vibrant Health
- ❏ Increased Alertness and Awareness
- ❏ Sense of Emotional Well-Being
- ❏ Great Feeling
- ❏ Improved Sex Life
- ❏ Calmer Mind
- ❏ Preventive Medicine

A question I'm commonly asked is "Why should I get a massage?" My first reply is "because it feels so good". If massage offered no more than that, I would still recommend it. When your life starts going too fast and you feel like you're beginning to lose control, a soothing, healing massage can bring you back to your center, to the place where life makes sense and you can think more clearly. It is so much easier to make decisions and handle the everyday crises that always seem to arise if you have a relaxed and calm mind. The best medical doctors will recommend massage before tranquilizers.

If your doctor is unaware of the benefits of massage, please give him this book. Massage has been more widely accepted in Europe. In Germany, doctors and massage therapists work together and the cost of massage is covered under their national health plan. In North America, many chiropractors work closely with massage therapists referring massage so it can be covered by insurance and health plans.

Massage can change your life. It is possible to get locked into cycles of pain. The stiff neck, the tense shoulders, the upset stomach are all reactions to the stresses and pressures of life that become reflected and locked into the body.

Tension, or holding muscles tight, can become so habitual that we forget we're even experiencing it.

Many times, I've worked on clients who thought they were relaxed, only to find their bodies stiff and sore. One man in particular comes to mind. It was his first massage, a gift from a friend. He told me "I consider myself relaxed and healthy and I am only accepting this massage to pacify my friend." As he lay on the massage table and closed his eyes, he continued to tell me how relaxed he was. As I cradled his head in my hands and touched his neck, I noticed the muscles in his neck were as stiff as boards. Obviously, he wasn't in high rapport with his body.

I decided to try an experiment. I gently and slowly slid my hands away from his head. The muscles in his neck were so tight and locked up that to my amazement, his head stayed elevated off the massage table. I was curious and I wanted to see how long he would hold his head this way. I watched for a full ten minutes and then I couldn't stand it any more. I worked on his neck and helped him to get in touch with those muscles, to let go and to relax. I believe, if I had permitted him, he would have held his head up off the massage table, without being aware of what he was doing, for the whole hour. The same was true for his whole body. Everywhere, there were tight painful muscles that he was unaware of. At the end of the massage, he floated off the massage table. He commented that he felt so light and free, like he had a new body. Most of us wear a suit of armor made up of tight muscles. When we are faced with a stressful situation we instinctively tighten our muscles, bracing ourselves against a real or imagined attack. When the stressful situation is over we forget to relax our muscles and become locked into holding patterns which block the natural flow of life. With the help of massage, we can free ourselves, letting go of painful holding patterns. Then life can be experienced anew.

Almost all of us go through some time in life holding parts of our bodies tight without knowing it. Over time, our bodies become locked into unnatural holding patterns that affect our posture and how we feel about ourselves. Try this experiment—stand up, push your stomach out, let your chest cave in, and let your shoulders and head drop forward. Hold this posture for a few minutes and notice how you feel. Now, take a deep breath, relax, and imagine a weight pulling down from the bottom of your spine while you are being pulled up by a string attached to the back of your head. Take a deep breath and let your chest expand. Relax your shoulders and let everything else fall into place. Hold this position a few minutes. How does it feel? How is it different from the first experience? Which one do you prefer and which one do you think would better help you to live a happier, more fulfilled life?

Massage therapy can help us relax and align our body posture by letting go of unconscious holding patterns that adversely affect the way we feel about ourselves and the way we feel about life. Our thoughts and our self-image are directly connected to our bodies. Patterns of negative thinking and poor self-image can be changed by releasing the corresponding patterns in the body.

Tight muscles in the body can constrict the flow of blood to our cells. A fresh supply of blood is needed to bring essential nutrients to our cells and to facilitate the exchange of waste products. Lethargy, a foggy mind, and memory loss are all a result of improper circulation. Massage can help increase the circulation of the blood and lymph resulting in a clearer, calmer mind and vibrant health. Massage cannot take the place of exercise and body movement, the natural way of increasing circulation, but it can supplement the exercise we get and help in those times when we're inactive.

Our bodies have been designed for radiant health. Most of us settle for far less. The human body was not made for sustained periods of inactivity.

Working in a job where we sit all day, or sitting at home in front of the television set too much of the time, is unhealthy. Our body needs movement. When we exercise, our muscle contractions help circulate the blood and the lymph fluids. Proper circulation of blood and lymph is vital for proper health.

Massage is also great for those times we over-exercise or over-use the body. Recovery time can be much quicker, as massage moves metabolic waste products out of the muscles and brings in fresh new blood.

Most people are surprised when I mention that their aches and pains may have an emotional cause. Thoughts and feelings are energy. Every time we have a thought or feeling that we suppress, that energy is stored somewhere in the body. We all have our weak points, the place where the energy goes when we have reached our threshold of stress.

Where is it for you? Your neck, shoulders, stomach, hands, or are you unaware of where your body holds tension? For some people, it's in the muscles around the eyes. Most vision problems are due to tension and holding of the muscles in and around the eyes. In the past months, I've had a 30 percent increase in my vision due to massage and specific exercises which relax the eyes and allow them to return to spontaneous, natural, clear vision. At this point, I am able to relax and let go enough to see 20/20 on an eye chart, but I haven't yet learned how to maintain that relaxation throughout the day.

Legally, no health professional can make claims of healing, but massage can help a whole array of illnesses and imbalances in the body. The cells of our bodies all have a positive and negative charge; we are electrical in nature. These charges create an electromagnetic field around our body, that can be photographed with Kirlian Photography. Blockages in the electromagnetic field show up as tender, painful areas, or as disease. Massage can and does facilitate the flow of energy in the body. Letting go and relaxing allows the body to return to its natural, spontaneous state of vibrant health.

Your body knows how to heal and repair itself. Of course, for healing massage to be maximally effective, it has to be supplemented with proper nutrition, a positive mental attitude, a balanced lifestyle which includes time for rest and family, and a healthy spiritual life.

I've seen people let go of emotional garbage and make positive changes in their lives through massage. There's a magic that happens in massage that is hard to put into words. I want you to experience it—take a chance. Go ahead and set an appointment for a massage, now!

Self-Test - Do I Need Massage?

A simple test to determine if massage would be beneficial for you: think about the past year and rate yourself by using the following scale.

O = Not true for me
5 = Slightly true for me
6 = Generally true for me
7 = Very true for me

_____ 1. I get sick two or more times a year.
_____ 2. I feel pressured.
_____ 3. I get headaches.
_____ 4. I sometimes wake up tired or exhausted.
_____ 5. I seem to forget things more.
_____ 6. I have trouble falling asleep.
_____ 7. I have gastro-intestinal problems.
_____ 8. I have high blood-pressure.
_____ 9. I have aches and pains.
_____ 10. I feel alone and unconnected.
_____ 11. I have anxiety attacks.

____ 12. I sometimes feel tired and worn out.
____ 13. I'm less enthusiastic about life.
____ 14. I worry more.
____ 15. My neck and shoulders feel tight.
____ 16. I feel burnt out by day's end.
____ 17. My sex drive has changed.
____ 18. I have more trouble focusing.
____ 19. My mind is not as clear as it used to be.
____ 20. I don't seem to have enough time to do what I want.

____ TOTAL SCORE

What your score means:

1-20 **Excellent.** You're really taking care of yourself.

21-50 **Normal.** A massage session would be therapeutic and fun.

51-75 **Caution area.** Time to take some action and get your life in control. Slow down a little and get a massage.

76-99 **Burn-out area.** You may be about to have some serious health problems. Time to re-evaluate your life and get a massage now.

100 + **Danger zone.** Did you really score over 100? It is time to make some major changes in your life. Get a massage today!

"Massage can help mankind

from the isolation and inhumanity

of the modern condition."

Dr. Katsusuke Serizawa

How Do I Get Started?

Choosing your massage therapist is very important. He or she will become one of your closest and most trusted friends over the course of time. On a personal level, you must like and trust your therapist in order for massage to be as effective as possible.

There are many different types of massage and bodywork. Bodywork is a term many times used interchangeably with massage. In my experience, the best massage therapists are eclectic, mixing and using the best elements from the different styles of massage. Massage and chiropractics go hand in hand, so start your search by asking your chiropractor or health care professional. Ask your friends, personal referrals are the best. Look on the bulletin board at your local health food store. Be aware when looking in the yellow pages.

In some parts of the country, some of the ads may be for escort services rather than for professional massage therapists.

To find a reputable message therapist contact:

In the U.S.A.:

American Massage Therapy Association
1130 W. North Shore Ave.
Chicago, Illinois 60626-4670
(312) 761-2682
                or
Associated Bodywork and Massage
 Professionals Inc.
P.O. Box 1869
Evergreen, Colorado 80439-1869
(303) 674-8478

In Canada:

Canadian Massage Therapist Alliance
456 Danforth Avenue
Toronto, Ontario, Canada M4K 1P4
(416) 463-7837

By contacting the above organizations, you can rest assured that your massage therapist will be a trained professional.

Massage can be received in your home or at your therapist's office. Before the session, your therapist will ask you a few questions or have you fill out a brief medical history. It's important to let your therapist know why you are there. Your therapist will leave the room so you can undress in private. During the massage, you will be draped with a towel or a sheet so only the part of your body being worked on will be uncovered.

Massage sessions usually last one hour, and during that time, you can expect one of the most pleasant experiences of your life. Your therapist will locate your aches and pains and help you to relax and release them. As your body relaxes, your mind will also relax. *Peaceful* is the best way I can describe the state you will experience.

Everyone Can Massage

And now the best part of all! You don't have to hire a trained professional to experience the healing benefits of massage. Anyone can do massage in their own home. All you need are your hands and the intention to help. Everyone can touch. Recently, after too many hours on the telephone, I developed a stiff neck. I had my four-year old son, Daniel, work on my neck and it was great. Fifty percent of the discomfort left immediately and he's never had any massage training. It is the intention to help and the caring that allow the magic of massage to happen.

Love is the most important part of any healing. We're all capable of loving, so we're all capable of healing. Directing this love through our hands is a natural instinct as old as mankind. Think of it, if you hurt yourself, your hands naturally go to the place of pain. That's why we hold our head when we have a headache. Placing your hands on another with love allows a wonderful healing energy to flow through you.

Trust yourself and your instincts. Let your hands be guided by your heart and your intuition. Know that if your intention is to help and you come from that deep loving place inside your heart, you can't do anything wrong. Massage is safe; you can't hurt anyone.

What better gift is there, or way to say I really care, than through sharing a massage with someone you love. After a tiring day at work or at school, a quick massage will uplift and revitalize you and your loved ones. Massage is great preventive medicine and many colds can be avoided just by eliminating accumulated stress with massage. Most children love to be touched; a quick massage is a great way to let your children know you really love them.

By the way, if you take the time to talk to your children, you will find out that they are under terrible stress. The social pressures, the increased expectations and work loads at school, and our rapidly changing and unstable society are leaving our children feeling stressed out and alienated. Through massage, you can open up levels of communication that didn't exist before.

I strongly believe that every household should have a massage table and a room or a place set aside for healing.

Massage is increasingly becoming a household word, and soon, massage will be as commonplace in our homes as is exercise equipment or the jacuzzi.

Reach Out
And
Touch
Someone

Massage Tables and Supplies

If you have an interest in healing and massage, I suggest you purchase a quality massage table. Your table will become the best investment in your health and happiness that you've ever made. Your table should be strong and light-weight, so you can transport it easily. You want it to be very comfortable so as to increase your enjoyment of massage. It's very important that your massage table have adjustable-height legs so that different people can use it.

You should use a high quality massage oil, many of which have added healing properties through the addition of herbs and aromatic essential oils. Never use mineral oil as it clogs the pores of the skin.

There are many excellent video tapes and books available, to help you get started in massage, that cover the whole range of massage from the total beginner to advanced techniques.

Most importantly, have fun! Laughter is the best way to free up healing energy. In massage, there is no right and wrong. If it feels good, it probably is good. Use your common sense and ask your partner if what you are doing feels right.

After playing with massage at home for awhile, you may want to have some formal training. There are many excellent schools throughout the country that offer programs ranging from the one-evening workshops to two-year professional training. Being a massage therapist is one of the most rewarding careers available.

My hope is that you reach out and touch someone today. Realize that we all are healers, and that healing is a natural, instinctive talent we all possess. This talent or gift needs only to be developed and the best way to develop it is to use it. The easiest way to use it is through touch. Good luck in your healing journey.

For help in selecting massage tables, oils, instructional books, and video tapes, call or write:

EARTHLITE MASSAGE TABLES, INC.
120 N. Pacific St., Suite L-7
San Marcos, CA 92069
Toll-free telephone, (Canada & U.S.A.)
(800) 872-0560

DR. GILLES A. LAMARCHE

Dr. Lamarche was born and raised in Timmins, Ontario, Canada. He attended the University of Toronto and graduated with a B.Sc. in 1975. He completed his post-graduate work at The Canadian Memorial Chiropractic College with a D.C., in 1979.

He has been in private practice in Northern Ontario since completing his Doctor of Chiropractic.

He is a member of the C.M.C.C. Governor's Club, is a pioneer of the Parker College of Chiropractic, is an active member of the Parker

School for Professional Success and a Parker management consultant. The Parker Chiropractic Resource Foundation awarded Dr. Lamarche its Chiropractor of the Year award for Canada in 1988.

Dr. Lamarche is quickly becoming a recognized speaker in biomechanics, back care, and positive lifestyles. He is the author of the book *The Doctor's Guide to Prescribing and Dispensing Orthotics*, and is presently working on a third book entitled *Lifestyles for Vibrant Health*.

You may contact him by writing to: Dr. Gilles A. Lamarche, Lamarche Chiropractic and Sports Injuries Clinic, 17 Cedar Street North, Timmins, Ontario, Canada P4N 6H8, or by telephoning (705) 264-1555.

*"The Doctor of the future
will give no medicine
but will interest his patients
in the care of the human frame,
in diet,
and in the cause
and the prevention
of disease."*

Thomas Edison

3 | THE WONDER OF CHIROPRACTIC

The Gift Of Health

Many people will tell you that the most precious thing in life is your health. Just ask anyone whose health is failing what they want most of all and they will tell you without hesitation, "My health". You have probably experienced the feeling many times yourself; how great it feels after recovering from a severe cold, or after a sprained ankle has healed and you are able to function without any discomfort. Good health is something healthy people take for granted, and something sick people always hope for.

Have you ever stopped for a moment to ask yourself why we get sick? Why, for example, does an individual live the first four or five decades of his life appearing completely healthy and all of a sudden dies of a massive heart attack? Why does a virus or bacteria create sniffles in one child and a serious disease in a sibling? Is it not logical to assume that if an individual is born completely normal, with all systems functioning to the optimum, that this individual is healthy and should in fact live a long life and die healthy? Would it not be normal to recognize that death is nothing other than part of the great master plan of life? If science today tells us that the human body is made to last 120 to 150 years, why then is this not the case?

These questions make it somewhat difficult to get a complete description of health and disease. It also becomes apparent that even the great nations of Canada and the United States of America, where the greatest resources of scientific minds and technology are found, are also, according to the World Health Organization of the United Nations, statistically the unhealthier countries of the world. Society has come to recognize health as being simply the absence of disease. Due to the quick-fix theory, people have come to think that the answer to all ailments can be found in the utilization of a drug or chemical.

Rather than looking for the cause of health, science has appeared to concentrate on trying to find the cause of disease and on defining the ability to fight this disease. It is quite strange that science appears to blame most of these processes on viruses and bacteria; but in looking at exposure, we find that one individual exposed to the exact same pathogen will be seriously ill, while another is unaffected. It has also been found by science that many individuals harbor very serious pathogenic bacteria while being completely asymptomatic. If we were to accept that the primary causes of disease are viruses and bacteria, how do we explain the cause of various pathologies known to man in which no virus or bacteria can be found?

In the book *Man's Greatest Gift to Man*, Dr. F. P. DeGiacomo utilizes the following analogy and I quote,

> We give credit for healing to outside factors which, in fact, have not been established as valid or effective. I like to think of the analogy where an individual who cuts himself runs to the nearest medical doctor. The doctor attends the injury by first cleansing it with some type of antiseptic, shoots the body full of antibiotics for the prevention of a possible infection, wraps the injury in sterile gauze, and the patient is told to come back in a week's time. Sure enough, after one week, the sterile bandages are removed and the lesion is healed. In turn, we are very grateful for the antibiotics, antiseptics and sterile bandages.
>
> May I suggest that you take a piece of meat out of the freezer, put a cut into it with a knife, then cleanse it with antiseptics, shoot it full of antibiotics and wrap it in a sterile gauze and bandages and put it away for a week's time. After one week, you will be surprised to find that

no healing took place, the lesion has remained, and the cut is still quite obvious. As unusual as this analogy may seem, you may say that it's totally absurd that a piece of meat could ever possibly heal because it is dead. This is the very point being made at this time. It is life that heals. There is no known antibiotic, no known drug, no known hindsight force or factors that ever healed. Only this thing called life has the ability and the power to heal and cure.

What then is this thing called life? There is only life in matter when life flows into and through it, giving it motion, action, and animation. Life may, therefore, be best described in simplest terms as a force, an energy, or an intelligence. This intelligence has often been referred to as innate intelligence, meaning an intelligence coming from within. This innate intelligence of a human body is good, constructive, helpful, and totally intelligent. It always does the right thing at the right place, at the right time, in the right quantities and qualities, providing there is no interference. Based on the appreciation of life, it is sound to reason that health comes from the inside out and not from the outside in.

Healing must, therefore, take place from an internal environment within man and cannot be introduced from the outside. Some people wish to refer to innate intelligence as simply nature or

God.   Regardless, we recognize that we are
dealing with a constructive force that maintains
what we recognize as health and life. When was
the last time you looked at a newborn baby and
appreciated this child for more than the outside
physical appearance and beauty? When was the
last time that you realized that total perfection
and total health of a newborn baby, recognizing
that 40 weeks prior, 2 cells came together, and
following multiple divisions, formed the first
recognizable tissue known as the neural streak?

The neural streak in time becomes the spinal
cord, and from this, all cells begin to differentiate
to become the tissues forming the organs and all
parts of the body. How is it that these cells know
exactly what to become and where to go and how
to function when they come together? How is it
that all this cellular formation does not end up in
chaos, but rather ends up in an intelligent form
called the human being? Is it not conceivable,
through logical reasoning, that this human being,
so intelligently created, must inherently possess
that very intelligence to maintain itself in a state
of health?

All bodily functions in a human being are
under the direction of the nervous system.   In
dealing with innate intelligence, we are concerned
primarily with the function of the central nervous

system, which involves the human brain and the spinal cord. The messages that originate in the brain travel down the spinal cord and branch out to give energy and life force to every single tissue and every single cell in the wonderful apparatus called the human being. This nerve energy or innate intelligence allows every tissue and every organ, to function in harmony with the total being. B. J. Palmer, one of the fathers of chiropractic, beautifully describes the human being as follows:

> Living man is the original and the first internal automatic autonomous automobile. Living man has a spiritual, mental generator and batteries (the brain), wire system (the nerves), spark plugs (peripheral ends of nerves), and trillions of motors (muscles). Living man is a chemical laboratory, mixing proper and right quantities and qualities and ingredients, acids and alkalies, at proper places, at correct times, to meet every necessity, to produce its own internal gasoline.

> Living man is the original internal combustion engine, producing a liquid and a gaseous heating and cooling system for all its parts; from which there is a carbon dioxide exhaust, which is transported through tubes to mufflers (lungs), which silently convey it to outer space... Living man is a spiritual, mental, electrical, chemical, mechanical, inter-related, inter-locking, integrated system, into one harmonious whole without conflict, each part of which works at the proper

place, at the right time, in normal quantities, with natural directions, both efferent and afferent, all of which works under one consistent guiding intelligence factor, all of which works as one total unit producing a moveable, healthy, living man.... Every intellectual, mental, electrical, mechanical, chemical fact known to science is first found working in living man.

Recognizing the very importance of the central nervous system, being the master control system of the human body, nature in her wisdom has protected the brain via a solid skull, and the spinal cord via the bony masses of the spinal column. The spinal column is comprised of: seven vertebrae in the neck referred to as the cervical spine; twelve vertebrae in the mid-region of the spinal column referred to as the thoracic spine; and five in the lower back referred to as the lumbar spine.

To provide communication from the brain to all the tissues and tissue cells as previously mentioned, nature provided openings on each side between each vertebra to allow the exit of the branches of the spinal cord.

VERTEBRAL SUBLUXATION AND NERVE CHART

A Vertebral Subluxation Complex (VSC, Bio-Mechanical Lesion) has numerous components, i.e. osseous (bone), neurological (nerve), connective tissue (muscles, ligaments and discs), lymphatic, circulatory, biomechanical alterations (curvatures, etc.), and somato-visceral (tissue, organs, etc.), which may cause irritation and/or compression of nerve roots and affect these components.[1] The nervous system controls and coordinates all organs and structures of the human body. Many nerves come from the spinal cord, pass through foramina (holes) formed by notches of 24 vertebrae in the movable spinal column, and innervate or supply specific areas and parts of the body.[2] Whenever specific areas or parts of the body are malfunctioning, generalized and/or specific symptoms are possible.[3]

SPINAL VERTEBRAE	Spinal Nerves	Areas and Parts of Body	Possible symptoms
CERVICAL SPINE (NECK)	1C	Back of the head	Headaches (including migraines, aches or pains at the back of the head, behind the eyes or in the temples, tension across the forehead, throbbing or pulsating discomfort at the top or back of head)
	2C	Various areas of the head	Jaw muscle or joint aches or pains
	3C	Side and front of the neck	Dizziness, nervousness, vertigo
	4C	Upper back of neck	Soreness, tension and tightness felt in back of neck and throat area
	5C	Middle of neck and upper part of arms	Pain, soreness, and restriction in the shoulder area
	6C	Lower part of neck, arms, and elbows	Bursitis, tendonitis
	7C	Lower part of arms, shoulders	Pain and soreness in arms, hands, elbows and/or fingers
	1T	Hands, wrists, fingers, thyroid	Chest pains, tightness or constriction
	2T	Heart, its valves and coronary arteries	Asthma, difficult breathing
	3T	Lungs, bronchial tubes, pleura, chest	Middle or lower mid-back pain, discomfort and soreness
THORACIC SPINE (MID-BACK)	4T	Gall bladder, common duct	

Level	Area	
7T	Pancreas, duodenum	Heart
		Lungs
8T	Spleen, lower mid-back	Gall bladder
		Liver
9T	Adrenal glands	Stomach
		Pancreas
10T	Kidneys	Spleen
		Adrenal glands
11T	Ureters	Kidneys
12T	Small intestines, upper/lower back	Small and large intestines
1L	Iliocecal valve, large intestines	Sex organs
		Uterus
2L	Appendix, abdomen, upper leg	Bladder
		Prostate glands
3L	Sex organs, uterus, bladder, knees	Low back pain, aches and soreness
4L	Prostate gland, lower back	Trouble walking
		Leg, knee, ankle and foot soreness and pain
5L	Sciatic nerve, lower legs, ankles, feet	Sciatica, pain or soreness in the hip and buttocks
SACRUM	Hip bones, buttocks	Rectal Trouble
COCCYX	Rectum, anus	

LUMBAR SPINE (LOW BACK)

SACRUM & COCCYX (PELVIS)

For further explanation of chart, ask your Doctor of Chiropractic.

[1] Murkowski, K.S.J.: *Collected Works — Vertebral Subluxation Complex*, 1988-1990.
[2] *Gray's Anatomy*, 29th Edition. Page 4. Note: Neurological innervation of the spinal nerves of the human body overlap in its supply to different areas and parts of the body as well as differ somewhat in different persons. This chart is a simplification of actual innervation. It has been designed for ease of layman's understanding and general edification and is not meant and should not be construed as anatomically accurate in its specific sense.
[3] Leach, Robert A.: *The Chiropractic Theories—A synopsis of scientific research*, 2nd Edition. Baltimore, Williams & Wilkins, 1986©.
Note: The possible symptoms listed on this chart are not meant and should not be construed to mean that all these possible symptoms are produced whenever there is a vertebral subluxation complex at a specific vertebral level or that chiropractic care will correct all of these conditions.

©1975, 1991 Parker Chiropractic Resource Foundation

#1300090

These openings become passage ways for the nerve to exit and bring all energy to all tissues of the human body. This network presents a communication system from the brain, down the spinal cord, to the spinal nerves and to all organs and tissue cells of the human body.

In order for the human body to function, communication must exist continuously between the brain and the cellular structures, and then from the cellular structures back to the brain. If interference occurs along the pathway in this communication system, the end tissue cell will be deprived of its required neurological energy, and will, consequently, malfunction. Interference usually occurs as the nerves exit between the vertebrae, due to a displacement of one or more vertebrae, and is referred to as a subluxation.

SUBLUXATION

The following illustration shows a mis-alignment of a vertebra from the one above and the one below, causing nerve impingement.

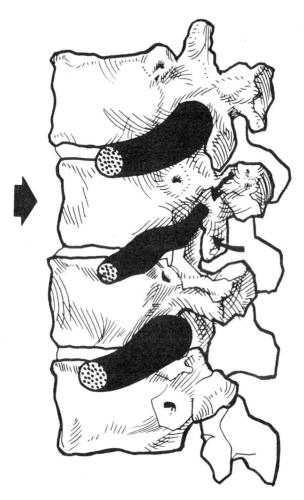

This causes interference with nerve impulses from the brain down the spinal cord to the tissue cell or from the tissue cell back to the brain. This subluxation may cause either reduced energy flow or irritation causing increased energy, hyperactivity and malfunction. It is easy to recognize that if this energy flow is increased or reduced, normal organic or cellular function cannot occur. This invariably leads to decreased tissue resistance, making the organs more susceptible to malfunction and disease. It is understandable that if optimum energy is not quickly regained, the patient will become ill. This illness may take years and even decades to manifest itself.

However, if the neurological interference is corrected and normal energy flow occurs, healing of the tissue should follow. The correction of a subluxation by the chiropractor, therefore, leads to restoration of vertebral function which in turn leads to restoration of normal energy flow. At that point, innate intelligence can once again become the director of healing and curing of the human body. This is why so many people get well under chiropractic care when other therapies have completely failed. This human energy—innate intelligence—flows from above, down, and inside out. None comes from the outside in. If any function in the human body is reduced or absent, at any time, in part or totally, the final manifestation is that of sickness or death.

You may now realize that sickness or disease is simply an absence of health—and not that health is the absence of sickness or disease. Life is energy, life is force, life is health. If you interfere with the expression of this energy, the human body cannot and will not function at its optimum potential. Once this potential is reduced as a result of a subluxation, the human body becomes a perfect environment for disease. In order for any disease process to flourish, such as virus or bacteria, the tissue resistance of the host must be reduced.

This concept will no doubt appear very simple to most people. Though the human body comprises a series of very complex structures and complex functions, there is no doubt that nothing can continue to function if there is no communication. Communication can only occur if the pathways of nerve energy from the brain to the tissue cells are completely clear of any interference. Subluxations are responsible for imbalance of internal harmony in the human being. By removing this interference, the body then possesses the ability, through its use of innate intelligence, to re-establish the processes required to achieve health. Thomas Edison was no fool when he suggested that the doctor of the future would concern himself with the care of the human frame.

Chiropractic - A Look Back

Research has let us recognize that the process utilized by the modern day chiropractor, that of a vertebral adjustment, has existed for thousands of years. Tissue manipulation is demonstrated by the ancient Chinese Kung Fu document which was written about 2700 B.C., some 4700 years ago. There is evidence that the Greeks, the ancient Japanese, Indians of Asia, as well as the early Egyptians and Babylonians, all practised the art of manipulation in one way or another. Physicians in ancient India appeared to manipulate the spine to relieve sickness, often meeting with marvellous results. It is also quite interesting to note that the ancient doctors of India, knowing nothing of the nervous system, traced cause and effect from misplaced vertebrae to organs and parts of the body affected.

The well-known father of medicine, Hippocrates, always reminded his students not to interfere in any way with nature's attempt towards recovery. He stressed that man must be treated as a whole, and the ultimate curative forces are within; we should study the entire patient in his environment; we should approach sickness with the eye of the naturalist. Hippocrates wrote a number of books on healing, including *Manipulation and Importance to Good*

Health, and *Of Setting Joints by Leverage*. He is also credited with emphasizing the importance of the spine. He said, "Get knowledge of the spine, for this is the requisite for many diseases". This is the basis on which modern chiropractic has evolved since its inception in 1895. The founder of chiropractic, Dr. Daniel David Palmer, defined chiropractic as follows:

> *Chiropractic is the name of a systematized knowledge of the science of life— biology, and a methodical comprehension and application of adjusting anatomical displacements; the cause of biological abnormalities, also an explanation of the methods used to relieve humanity of suffering, and the prolonging of life.*

His son, Dr. B. J. Palmer, who further advanced chiropractic, defined chiropractic as follows: "Chiropractic is a philosophy, science and art of things natural; a system of adjusting the segments of the spinal column by hand only, for the correction of dis-ease." By definition, according to B. J. Palmer, the adjusting of vertebrae that interferes with the conductive tissues, until such time that the vertebrae no longer interferes with the conductive tissues, is natural, is done by hand only, and is chiropractic.

Today, it is commonly accepted that disease may be caused by disturbance of the nervous system. While other factors may impair man's health, disturbance of the nervous system remains the most important factor in the etiology of disease. The nervous system is responsible for all adaptation and coordination of events that control cellular activities. Disturbances of the nervous system may cause or aggravate disease in any part of the human body.

Subluxations leading to improper neurological function may occur as a result of poor posture, strains and sprains, asymmetrical activities, developmental defects, chemical, or psychic irritations, stress, and poor nutrition. You may think of many other physical, chemical, or psychological factors which may lead to vertebral subluxations, and invariably to improper nervous system function and ill health.

Many times, interference factors will cause obstructions in the conduction of innate forces. When the supply is equal to demand, the organism lives in total health. What greater benefit could be done for the human being than to remove any obstructions to life?

When chiropractic is given a chance to utilize fully the 33 Principles of Chiropractic (see

Appendix at the end of this chapter), to subject the world population to its great value, and given a chance to perform its many miracles, chiropractic could reduce to a minimum abnormalities which exist among the human race.

In this day and age, this would not only create a great economic saving, but also lead to a healthy environment and a healthy life of millions. Chiropractic is a way of life in accordance with the principles of life. It may be difficult for the uninitiated to digest, but these are the facts, this is human existence. Chiropractic has passed the test of time and welcomes all who seek better health.

Chiropractic Today

Chiropractic has become a firm part of the health care delivery system in the world today. There is evidence of its acceptance by individuals, by government, by institutions—both educational and social—and by the general public. Though many have never attended a chiropractor and may not understand the philosophy and *modus operandi* of chiropractic, in North America, most can tell you a story about themselves, a friend, or a relative who has had a successful experience with chiropractic.

It is from individual patients that chiropractic has found its greatest support. Many patients have been willing to defend and fight for the value of chiropractic health care. Three distinguished researchers from the University of Toronto worked for one year to research and present the facts, and only the facts, about a distinctive form of health care which has survived a century of hostile criticism from the medical world—called chiropractic.

The results of the research were published in the book, *Chiropractors Do They Help?* Doctors Kelner, Hall and Coulter found the realities of chiropractic to be far removed from the rhetoric. They found chiropractic to be far from "unscientific", and that the training of today's chiropractors involves a complete course in basic sciences followed by all the facts in relation to the art, philosophy, and science of chiropractic. The authors presented a picture of a practitioner who functions without relying on drugs and surgery. The chiropractor's patients, having found no relief in allopathic (traditional) medicine, are victims of the gaps in the medical system, and seek successful alternatives.

Contrary to popular myth, these patients come from all walks of life and are rational and sophisticated in their use of health care. The public's attitude towards health care, "one of our most colossal industries", has traditionally been one of heavy reliance on medical science. In the decade of the 80's and now of the 90's, this is changing, and medical science per se is being seriously challenged.

Chiropractic care is distinctive in terms of its techniques of treatment, its selective body of knowledge and its system of beliefs about health and healing. Chiropractic offers to the patient holistic health care. It normally goes beyond treatment to the total benefit of the patient, offering advice on prevention of potential future problems and the maintenance of good health. Chiropractic is considered conservative and often preventative care. The procedures are low-risk and aimed at conserving health and avoiding treatment which may have negative side effects.

In general, chiropractors have made a point of ensuring their patients of their availability, starting early in the morning and often working late into the evening. As a rule, chiropractic and chiropractors tend to offer immediate care. There is no prolonged waiting list or testing required before treatment can begin. Research has shown that chiropractic care usually leads to early relief, often providing restoration of function. Chiropractors, as a population, approach their patients with personal orientation and personalized attitudes. Most chiropractors are known as the doctor who really cares.

If you had the opportunity to see the film *The Doctor*, with William Hurt, you will no doubt remember that at the outset, they portrayed the doctor as treating the patient as a number or as a case. Once William Hurt experiences a personal illness, he appears to become much more personable and starts being concerned with the whole person involved in the doctor-patient relationship. This is the way chiropractic schools train their future chiropractors.

Chiropractors also have the notion that it is important for the patient to understand their injury or illness and therefore spend time explaining the cause, the treatment, and the consequences which will then ensue. Since it is very important for the patient to become pro-active in their lifestyles, chiropractors usually make a serious attempt to make patients aware of their personal role and responsibility in the maintenance of their own health care. Chiropractors participate as partners with their patients in their treatment and follow-up, to achieve good health.

Chiropractic schools stress the emphasis on the natural healing powers of the body and therefore present a distinctive orientation to their educational program. Medical schools, on the other hand, stress the importance of interventions designed to combat specific disease states, and this emphasis shapes medical training. Chiropractic education is geared towards producing practitioners who will be capable and suited to the rendering of care to the patient.

Though academic excellence is definitely a factor in selecting a prospective chiropractic student, all chiropractic colleges appear to understand the importance of the candidate's personality and general interest. Regardless of academic excellence, if a prospective student does not have the desire and the potential to give personalized care, this individual is usually rejected.

Though chiropractic for years seemed to be unscientific, due to its lack of scientific research, the decade of the 80's and the beginning of the 90's has changed this vision. Some of the most respected research projects have been published in these recent times. The most notable, published in June 1990 in the British Medical Journal, was a compilation of results involving a 10-year study comparing chiropractic care and traditional medical care in the treatment of acute and chronic low back pain. This research study, funded by the British Medical Research Council, showed that chiropractic was more effective, at a rate of 2:1, in the treatment of acute and chronic low back pain. Many such studies have shown the effectiveness of chiropractic care, and due to this recent positive information, more and more research is being done on the function of the spine and the validity of chiropractic. We are now in the decade where the health model will experience a major paradigm shift. Chiropractic and preventative health care will continue to grow as people become more aware of these valid principles.

Research is not the only thing that is creating this paradigm shift. In the past four or five years, much attention in North America has focused on the so-called war against drugs. From the drug lords of South America to the pushers in the cities and villages of North America, the talk is of removing drugs from the surface of the earth. The magnitude of the illegal trade is overwhelming and the consequences must not be ignored.

However, overshadowed by these headlines is another drug problem which is considered to be equally serious—the overuse and abuse of prescription and over-the-counter drugs. We are a world on medication. For most, from the day a child is born until the adult dies, a miracle cure is often sought for those evil pains. We have become a society of instant: instant coffee, instant potatoes, instant pill, instant cure. There are drugs that keep us awake and those that put us to sleep.

We suffer from obesity, high blood pressure, stress, and high cholesterol levels—all of which can be corrected with a change of lifestyle. Instead, the average human being chooses a new drug developed as an alternative to a healthy diet, regular exercise, and chiropractic care. Drugs have gradually become accepted as an integral part of our everyday lives. Sophisticated advertising campaigns, costing hundreds of millions of dollars, have convinced most people that prescription and over-the-counter drugs are both safe and effective.

Always remember, however, that the miracle drug of yesterday is no longer available today. The most accurate statement would be that in some cases, some people get some benefit from some drugs. The large drug manufacturer, Parke, Davis and Company, has previously admitted "There is a problem of toxicity with all drugs...it is a well established fact that there is no drug presently existing on the market which is devoid of harmful effects."

As chiropractors, we do not prescribe drugs; nor do we tell patients to stop taking their medication prescribed by another physician. We simply advocate the correction of the cause of the symptom, which usually eliminates the need for medication.

All drugs, whether over-the-counter, prescription, or illegal street drugs, have one thing in common: they can drastically alter the normal functioning of the body's cellular structure. In some cases, due to the severity of the symptom or disease which is past the point of natural healing, drugs can be helpful and occasionally life-saving. But in most cases, drugs have a negative impact on the individual's health, often leading to disastrous consequences. Not only do drugs inhibit the body's natural recuperative powers, but their side effects also can lead to other diseases referred to as Iatrogenic Diseases. Iatrogenic is defined as "being caused as a secondary effect of the prescribed treatment."

By choice, chiropractors do not prescribe drugs. Good health is not found in a tablet or in a bottle. Health comes from within and is a result of a positive lifestyle, free of interference, full of good nutrition, regular exercise, proper rest and positive mental attitude. Your body was designed to be a self-healing organism and will function that way naturally given the chance. Understanding the importance of an interrupted energy flow from brain cell to tissue cell, you will no doubt begin to understand the value of regular spinal check-ups and corrective chiropractic care when necessary. We do not need to be a nation on medication; we must rather be a nation concerned with the vitality of life and the tremendous value of health. By making sure that all interference to the stream of energy that flows from your brain through the spine to every cell of your body is eliminated, your body will be able to maintain its own health in a natural manner.

It is practically impossible to lead a life that is completely free of illness or injury. However, it is possible to minimize the effects of such setbacks by being healthy and by recognizing the positive efforts which keep you healthy. The way your body reacts is usually a reflection of how you live. Your lifestyle greatly determines how well you will be and how long you will live. Make chiropractic a part of that lifestyle and you will no doubt lead a healthier, happier, prolonged life.

In less than 100 years, chiropractic has become North America's second largest primary health care delivery system. Because chiropractic's positive and often dramatic results do not involve the use of drugs or surgery of any kind, it has been proven to be safer and more cost effective than traditional medicine. Unlike other forms of health care, which stimulate or inhibit the body's natural functions, chiropractic's scope is to remove interference to the normal healing process. Too often in the past, people have looked to chiropractic as a last resort. They spend time and money, and suffer needlessly, while trying to identify and treat a condition which might best be corrected with chiropractic adjustments. The chiropractic approach has helped millions of people achieve a better level of health, often after other methods have failed.

More and more people are making chiropractic their first choice for health care. Shouldn't you?

Chiropractic - The Next Generation

Our children are our future. Few people realize that the birth process is recognized as one of the foremost causes of early spinal subluxations. Even during normal and uncomplicated deliveries, the spine is subject to extreme pressures from contractions and pushing by the mother. The child may also experience severe traction to the neck from pulling, stretching, and twisting when being guided to enter this life. Studies are revealing that spinal degeneration and distortions, both in the young and the elderly, were probably present as young as infancy, and are often due to the birth process. These first subluxations, if left uncorrected, can result in serious nerve damage. Nerve interference and irritation from cervical spine trauma at birth is known to cause abnormal function, unusual behaviour, and sometimes, in extreme cases, premature death.

Abraham Towbin, M.D., while a neuropathologist at Harvard Medical School, found that nearly one in every three stillborn infants he examined appeared to have actually died of injuries to the cervical spine during childbirth. Dr. Towbin is one of the many world authorities who investigated the relationship between birth process and spinal damage. In one of his many published articles, he states: "During the last part of the delivery, during the final extraction of the fetus, mechanical stress imposed by obstetrical manipulation, even the application of standard orthodox procedures, may be intolerable to the fetus."

Dr. Towbin's studies have also established a link between birth trauma and Sudden Infant Death Syndrome (SIDS). SIDS, known by most as Crib Death, is a death of an apparently healthy infant which remains unexplained, even after routine autopsy.

Although Dr. Towbin's studies were originally challenged by others in the medical community, new studies have now confirmed that uncorrected subluxations "can cause incomplete or temporary compromise to the blood supply to the upper spinal cord." This leads to damage to the respiratory centre and appears to be a factor in SIDS cases.

Chiropractors have long advocated that children should have their spine examined as early as possible after birth. I personally checked my children moments after they were born and continue to do so on a regular basis. This has led these three children to enjoy a special state of health.

The early months in a child's life are critical to the formation of a stable, healthy, and resilient spine. Spinal adjustments, using very gentle techniques, are all that is required to correct subluxations in infants. Throughout chiropractic offices in this world, more and more parents are introducing their infants and children to the chiropractic method of health care because they know that the growing years are the most important years of a person's life.

As the saying goes, "As the twig is bent, so grows the tree." The next time you see a child falling from a skate board or a bicycle, try to recognize the twists and turns that exist in this fall. You will soon realize that chiropractic care is important and should be utilized in detecting and correcting any imbalances or misalignments which have occurred in the spine.

As parents, we are usually quick to treat the obvious scrapes, bruises, and cuts, but often do not notice the less obvious physical problems that the children may develop as they grow. You must remember that most often, children also do not know how to express the discomfort that they may be feeling. The subsequent moodiness, fatigue, lack of concentration, lowered resistance to disease, hyperactivity, or even episodes of bed-wetting often seem to be attributed to "growing pains". In most cases, they are in fact the result of spinal misalignment or subluxation.

I well remember the case of a young boy named Mario. After having been a straight "A" student from grade one to grade five, Mario began grade 6 and registered a "D" during the first semester. Not understanding what was happening to this child, and after a meeting with the teacher and principal, the mother decided to bring him to my office. After a consultation, the child related that he had had a fall from the barn loft during the month of July. Having been afraid to relate this to his parents, he simply went about his daily chores, never mentioning the incident.

Upon careful examination, we noticed a number of spinal subluxations, mostly in the upper cervical spine. After no more than four weeks of care, this young boy started improving his school performance and ended the year with an "A". He had been suffering from constant headaches and blurred vision, symptoms which he had not reported. You see by this example alone that proper spinal care is essential to a child's health. This includes special attention following the birth process and regular examinations and care throughout life.

If you are interested in being healthy for life, you should be interested in being a chiropractic patient for life. Most patients insist on having their children's teeth checked for cavities at least every six months, and neglect to have their children's spines examined for spinal subluxations. Always remember that chiropractic care is for everyone; remember that the integrity of the nervous system should never be compromised. Only a chiropractor is trained in the detection, location, and correction of spinal subluxations. Don't hesitate!

Conclusion

Critics call the present health care system in the world a disease care system, based on the mistaken belief that the best way to help is to spend even more money fighting disease. In actual fact, health is the natural state of the body, and sickness and disease are abnormal conditions that can often be corrected by the body's own in-born intelligence without the stimulation of drugs or the invasion of surgery.

Chiropractors promote a natural approach to achieving and maintaining good health. They believe that drugs or surgery should be used only after all other options have been exhausted or when a patient's life is being threatened. Throughout the years, the efforts of chiropractors have helped millions to achieve a better level of health, and today, chiropractic continues to expand and flourish as the second-largest health care profession in the world.

Always remember that people of all ages can achieve better health through chiropractic care, and should have chiropractic examinations. The primary role of the chiropractor is to locate, correct, and prevent spinal subluxations, so that every tissue and organ of the body is well connected and receives proper neurological control from the brain. Removal of nerve interference can bring dramatic improvements to a person's state of health and enhance resistance to infection and disease.

Regular chiropractic care can help people achieve and maintain a better level of health. There is no doubt that expanding the scope of available chiropractic services will help this world with the present health care crisis. Obviously, if people don't get sick as often because their nervous system is functioning properly, they won't require as many medical procedures.

A healthy person is not a burden on the present system. By emphasizing the prevention rather than the treatment of disease, chiropractors are leading the effort to bring costs under control and sanity back into what is still considered one of the best systems in the world. The recent research in Great Britain and a second study in Australia have both confirmed that chiropractic plays an important role in today's health care system, and chiropractic is often more effective and cost efficient than traditional medical care for a wide variety of ailments.

The British study suggests that increased chiropractic services would save millions in medical costs and social security payments. It would also result in a significant reduction in the number of days absent from work. One of the most positive findings of the Australian study was the level of satisfaction of the respondents who had been to a chiropractor. The majority reported that their visits had a substantial effect on their condition and stated that treatment had substantially improved their general health.

It is time for a change. It is time for all to wake up to the fact that chiropractic is scientifically valid, safe, effective, and cost-efficient. A comprehensive approach that encourages prevention over treatment of disease, and a system that rewards effective and cost-efficient techniques, can bring about significant change. Chiropractic is ready for the challenge. Is society ready for the change?

Appendix

The 33 *Principles of Chiropractic*
by Dr. F.P. DeGiacomo
Author, *Man's Greatest Gift To Man*

1. *The Major Premise*
A universal intelligence is in all matter and continually gives to it all its properties and actions, thus maintaining it in existence.

2. *The Chiropractic Meaning Of Life*
The expression of this intelligence through matter is the chiropractic meaning of life.

3. *The Union Of Intelligence And Matter*
Life is necessarily the union of intelligence and matter.

4. *The Triune Of Life*
Life is a triunity having three necessary united factors: intelligence, force, and matter.

5. *The Perfection Of The Triune*
In order to have 100 percent life, there must be 100 percent intelligence, 100 percent force, 100 percent matter.

6. *The Principle Of Time*
There is no process that does not require time.

7. *The Amount Of Intelligence In Matter*
The amount of intelligence for any given amount of matter is 100 percent and is proportional to its requirements.

8. *The Function Of Intelligence*
   The function of intelligence is to create force.

**9. *The Amount Of Force Created By
   Intelligence***
   *The amount of force created by intelligence is always
   100 percent.*

10. *The Function Of Force*
   *The function of force is to unite intelligence and
   matter.*

11. *The Character of Universal Forces*
   *Forces of universal intelligence are manifested by
   physical laws; they are unswerving and unadapted,
   and have no solicitude for the structures in which
   they work.*

12. *Interference Of Transmission Of Universal Forces*
   *There can be interference with transmission of
   universal forces.*

13. *The Function Of Matter*
   The function of matter is to express force.

14. *Universal Law*
   *Forces manifested by motion in matter; all matter has
   motion, therefore there is universal life in all matter.*

15. *No Motion Without The Efforts Of Force*
   *Matter can have no motion without the application of
   force by intelligence.*

16. Intelligence In Both Organic And Inorganic Matter

Universal intelligence gives force to both organic and inorganic matter. In organic matter, universal intelligence is in the form of an innate intelligence within that living thing, governing it through intelligent direction and organization. With inorganic matter, universal intelligence is manifested as an intelligent force maintaining molecular discipline and organization.

17. Cause And Effect

Every effect has a cause and every cause has an effect.

18. Evidence Of Life

The signs of life are evidence of the intelligence of life.

19. Organic Matter

The material of the body of a living thing is organized matter.

20. Innate Intelligence

A living thing has an inborn intelligence within its body called innate intelligence.

21. The Mission Of Innate Intelligence

The mission of innate intelligence is to maintain the material of the body of a living thing in active organization.

22. The Amount Of Innate Intelligence

There is 100 percent of innate intelligence in every living thing– the requisite amount, proportionate to its organization.

23. *The Function Of Innate Intelligence*
The function of innate intelligence is to adapt universal forces and matter for use in the body, so that all parts of the body will have coordinated action for mutual benefit.

24. *The Limits Of Adaptations*
Innate intelligence adapts forces and matter for the body as long as it can do so without breaking a universal law, or innate intelligence is limited by the limitations of matter.

25. *The Character Of Innate Forces*
The forces of innate intelligence never injure or destroy the structures in which they work.

26. *Comparison Of Universal And Innate Forces*
In order to carry on the universal cycle of life, universal forces are destructive and innate forces constructive, as we regard structural matter.

27. *The Normality Of Innate Intelligence*
Innate intelligence is always normal and its function is always normal.

28. *The Conductors Of Innate Intelligence*
The forces of innate intelligence operate through or over the nervous system in animal bodies.

29. *Interference With Transmission Of Innate Forces*
There can be interference with the transmission of innate forces.

30. *The Cause Of Dis-ease*

Interference with transmission of innate forces causes incoordination or dis-ease.

31. Subluxation

Interference with transmission in the body is always directly or indirectly due to subluxation in the spinal column.

32. *The Principles Of Coordination*

Coordination is the principle harmonious action of all the parts of an organism, in fulfilling their offices and purposes.

33. *The Law Of Demand And Supply*

The law of demand and supply is existent in the body in its ideal state, wherein the clearing house is the brain, innate the virtuous banker, brain cells clerks, and nerve cells messengers.

Bibliography

Bohemier, Dr. G. *The Spinal Column.* Editor, Winnipeg Manitoba.

The British Medical Journal. June 1990.

DeGiacomo, F.P. *Man's Greatest Gift To Man.* New York: LSR Learning Associates Inc., 1978.

Homewood, A.E. *The Neurodynamics of the Vertebral Subluxation.* 1962.

Kelner, Merrijoy, Hall, Oswald, Coalter, Ian. *Chiropractors, Do They Help?* Toronto: Fitzhenry and Whiteside, 1980.

Smith, David Chapman. *The Chiropractic Report.* Editor. Toronto

Stoner, Fred D.C. *The Eclectic Approach To Chiropractic.* F.L.S. Publsihing Company, Las Vegas Nevada, 1975.

Weilan, C.W., Goldschmidt, S. *Medicine and Chiropractic.* Lonbard IL: The National College of Chiropractic, 1979.

Wilk, Chester A. *Chiropractic For Pain, Headaches, and Stress.* Chicago IL, 1987.

Wilk, Chester A. *Chiropractic Speaks Out.* Park Ridge IL: Wilk Publishing Company, 1976.

"The health of the people

is really the foundation upon which

all their happiness

and all their powers as a state

depend."

Benjamin Disraeli

ANN RAYMER

Ann Raymer is a chiropractor, entrepreneur, and philanthropist. She was born and raised in Michigan and received her B.A. from the University of Michigan. She then spent one year in post-graduate studies at Wayne State University. She completed her pre-Chiropractic studies in Michigan and graduated Cum Laude from Western States Chiropractic College in Portland, Oregon in 1982.

She has been in private practice in Idaho for 10 years, where she has been using love as an essential element for healing. Besides her successful chiropractic practice, she is owner of Homecleaners Plus, and is currently developing her newest venture "Esteem Up".

She combines her love for humanity and nature in her philanthropic work. In 1989, she was given the prestigious Humanitarian Award by Ward Management Corporation, and for the last four years has been honored as a Benefactor of the Foundation for Chiropractic Education and Research.

You may contact her by writing to Ann Raymer, D.C., 803 South Jefferson, Suite 3, Moscow, Idaho, 83843-3723, or by telephoning (208) 882-3723.

4 LOVING THE HEALER WITHIN

Health

Health is often high on the scale of most people's values for a happy and productive life. If injury or illness occurs, then health usually becomes the top priority. Any of us who has ever experienced serious illness or injury, or observed it in others, is keenly aware of how dramatically it affects all areas of our life. Activity levels decline, personal relationships change and become strained, our enjoyment of the diversity of our lives narrows as though blinders were closing in beside our eyes until our focus is solely on ourselves. Just making it through the day becomes a major accomplishment.

The person suffering from pain, illness, or injury begins to take precedence over other family members, friends and co-workers. Their needs are seen as being greater, more demanding, and more immediate. (Somewhere at the back of our minds is the troubling awareness that the outcome of their condition could be death.)

These are the situations that bring forth the natural and strong desire to be helpful. Far too often, the opposite occurs, and we feel helpless, frustrated, and fearful. Too many of us believe that only health professionals know what to do to help, that we are only useful to wait upon the patient. Frequently, we oblige silently, feeling a lack of appropriate words or wisdom for the situation.

Our sense of powerlessness coupled with the extreme value we place on the health of ourselves or our loved ones is what has brought about the development of the extremely expensive technology that exists today. We are now allowed to look into the body in ways never before possible with the wonders of CT and MRI. Technology allows us to transplant organs and keep brain-dead bodies alive. This technology is of tremendous benefit to humanity, but we must beware of the possibility for separation from the human element. We must strive to use the technology appropriately to enhance the quality of life and preserve the dignity and integrity which is the essence of human life. There are certainly times when the technology itself becomes an object of fear because of misunderstanding, lack of communication, or misuse.

The separation, isolation and movement restriction involved in as non-invasive procedure as MRI may cause claustrophobia in patients who are unprepared. Simple considerations such as offering the patient earplugs to diminish the metallic hammering sound, and a one minute course in meditation, creative visualization or self-hypnosis, along with an accurate description of the patient's role in the procedure, would alleviate most of the fear.

Fear is the most dangerous response, whether it is of the procedure, the illness, or the injury. It is a dangerous response whether felt by the patient, family, or friends, and increasingly so, by the healing practitioner. In fear, the mind's imaginings can get out of control, rushing to the worst conclusions and into a downward spiral of negative thoughts. Fear is greater in those lacking in self-love, for these people seem to think that the worst outcome is *natural* or what they should expect, and even worse, what they somehow *deserve.* Fear impedes healing. It separates and shuts you away until you feel your chest constrict as though your heart were being gripped by an enormous fist.

The antidote to fear is faith. These two emotions are so diametrically opposed that your mind is unable to hold both at the same time.

Faith is the belief in things not yet seen, the belief that all things are working in divine order. Faith is believing that the healing that can take place will take place. Faith is even the belief that if death does occur, it is what is meant to be and that if illness lingers, there are more lessons to be learned. Faith is believing that "with God all things are possible". Or as the proverb states, *"Faith is the bird that feels the light and sings while the dawn is still dark."*

Closely aligned to faith is the other essential ingredient to awakening the healer within, that of self-love. As Dr. Robert Schuller has said ...

Self-love is not arrogance,

narcissism, self-glorification

nor self will.

Instead, self-love is a deep sense

of self-worth, or high self-esteem,

of trusting and honoring yourself,

of knowing, and without judging,

accepting yourself as you are.

Self-Love and Healing

Current thinking, whether scientific, secular, or theological, points to the importance of self-love in the healing process. Self-love, while seemingly a recent concept, born out of a relatively peaceful and spiritual environment, is at least as old as Christ's teachings to "love your neighbor as you love yourself."

Self-love is a process. It is a journey with a wonderful destination. For most of us, this journey begins when we realize that our internal dialogue is filled with negative judgments about ourselves and others at nearly every turn. Our silent self-talk is often worse than our outward expressions. With growing awareness that what we say to ourselves is indeed under our control, we can change the messages to ones of love, support, and acceptance. Cutting our finger while fixing dinner doesn't have to be followed by, "How stupid of me", but can call forth, "How unlike me, I'll slow down and be more careful now." We should practice an extension of the Golden Rule and do unto *ourselves* and others as we would have them do unto us.

Too often, we think, "Well, I'll love myself when I lose this extra weight, or when I quit smoking or when I get a job I like better." What we need to realize is that in this earthly, physical existence, we are at best imperfectly perfect, and the time to begin loving ourselves is now. We can still plan changes and improvements with increasing self-love as the first one to put in place. From there, we will see other real changes taking place as we change our habits, attitudes, and self-care. As children, what we wanted most was to be loved for who we were; as adults we can learn to do this for ourselves, and learning to love ourselves enables us to love others with greater ease.

Self-love can take many forms. It can be expressed through regular exercise or sufficient rest for the body, or a good diet. It shows through a good attitude and enjoyable stimulus for the mind and faith, joy and love for the spirit.

Self-love, as it increases, is what allows us to experience peace of mind, happiness, great relationships, joy, and good health for ourselves, and allows us to be able to give more to others. What formerly was only a desire to assist becomes loving and considerate words and actions.

As Leo Buscaglia says, "What harm can come from mutual respect, gentleness, goodness, trust, and peaceful co-existence?"

Before exploring the importance of loving the healer within, whether that healer is the patient, their loved ones, or the professional who has traditionally been considered the healer, let's think together about healing, what it is, and how it takes place.

Deepak Chopra says "It has always been known that healing is a process controlled by nature." We know from observation that most healing takes place naturally. The body doesn't have to be told how to heal a cut or get over a cold, even though we can assist it by keeping the cut clean and open to the air, or by resting and taking extra vitamins and liquid for the cold.

In chiropractic, our basic philosophy is that there is a universal and innate intelligence that guides all healing. Universal intelligence is what some would call God and others would call the natural laws governing all creation. Innate intelligence is that knowledge contained within each cell, organ, and organism that guides its activity and healing. We see the body as a fitting temple of the soul which should be cared for accordingly.

We also need to understand that healing is natural, but so are disease and death. As we find vaccines and cures for diseases, new ones appear to take their place as part of the natural order of ending our temporal lives.

Awaken Your Healing Ability Towards Yourself

"The natural healing force within each one of us is the greatest force in getting well."
                                            Hippocrates

Let's explore together how to awaken the healing force within if we find ourselves in the role of the patient.

Step 1

One action we can take is to begin listening to our bodies and spirits to discover what makes us feel better or worse. We should do this on all levels including the physical, mental, emotional, and spiritual.

Step 2

A second step is to focus on staying in a state of self-love, not judging or criticizing ourselves, but loving ourselves as we are. With self-love, we empower ourselves and let go of bad habits that have contributed to the illness or injury, and to adopt positive new habits. Increased self-love will also influence how much healing energy we will be able to receive from a health practitioner and from our family and friends.

Step 3

A third step is to take the responsibility to seek help from a health practitioner. In the same way that you probably wouldn't attempt, by yourself, to fix a serious problem with your computer, it's logical that you should consult a health care specialist when you have a problem with your health.

Many professionals agree that healing begins with making that phone call for an appointment, because it represents the patient's willingness to initiate the healing process. The healing power of taking action has been demonstrated in numerous studies on the effect of a placebo. Even though the placebo contains no medicinal substance, cures take place for some of the patients simply because they believe they are being treated for their condition. Doing anything proves far more effective than doing nothing.

Step 4

We can also awaken the healer within by becoming involved in our own care by following the health practitioner's advice regarding exercise, diet, and rest. These recommendations are derived from experience and expertise. Over the years I have noticed an appreciable difference in recovery between those patients who take an active role in their healing compared to those who do not. Sometimes that responsibility may be shown by simply keeping their appointments and arriving on time. At others it is by doing the recommended exercises regularly and by avoiding harmful activities.

Step 5

Letting go of fear is another step towards awakening and loving the healer within. I see my patients experiencing fear around many different issues, including a sense of their body betraying them because they are feeling pain. Actually, pain is the only way your body can talk to you when there has been a long-standing, underlying cause, and the proverbial straw has broken the camel's back. This is when symptoms begin to be felt in the form of pain.

Patients also have fears around their mental abilities. Pain often decreases their concentration and focus, and they complain of not being able to remember what it was they wanted to do when they enter a room. These are reasonably normal responses, because their minds are concentrating primarily on their pain and body, and on just being able to accomplish ordinary, daily activities.

There can be fear around whether they will be able to continue or resume their job duties. This is an extremely sensitive issue for men, who tend to derive more of their identity from their work than do women. The fear may revolve around sexual performance or participation in family life, like being able to lift a toddler or go on a vacation.

I often have patients who have already seen several other physicians without receiving any beneficial results. Fear has become a major issue with them. They sense a deep feeling of relief when the history and examination are done. They know that someone is genuinely listening to them and is going to take time to explain their problem and outline the treatment. Just knowing that someone cares and is going to be there for them brings a deep feeling of reassurance and begins to promote healing.

Step 6

One of the most effective ways of empowering our innate healing abilities is to develop and maintain a positive mental attitude. Positive expectation is critically important in the mind-body alliance of healing. We do have control over our conscious thoughts. We can use them to visualize the outcome we want and to affirm it with positive statements. These actions deal with our conscious mind, so if a positive mental attitude isn't working for you, you might consider that there may be blocks or stronger messages coming from the subconscious area of your mind. The illness, injury, or treatment may be serving as a catalyst for you to open up to and release the old, negative information.

Step 7

With self-love and loving support from others, we feel safe enough to view illness or injury as a teacher. It can help us reorder priorities in a meaningful way, or help us look at what we've been doing and how we may want to change. We examine our work and play habits, our diet, and attitude, and are able to see the counter-productive areas. It can help us develop the will-power and motivation to get rid of those bad habits. It can also prove to us the wisdom of doing the right things with regularity instead of inconsistency.

Step 8

Illness and injury can cause us to become more loving and compassionate, warmer, and more verbal. It seems to be a great equalizer putting us more in touch with the inter-relatedness of humanity. We are less embarrassed and confused with how to deal with illness when we have experienced it ourselves.

Step 9

Illness or injury can also help us to build our faith. We are all given challenges, and my personal belief is we are never given a challenge that is bigger than we can handle. If we choose to exercise faith as a basic part of our response to the challenge, it will grow as surely as any other skill we use.

Step 10

Another way we can develop our own healing ability is to ask our health practitioner for information so we have a useful understanding of our condition.   Ask for handouts from associations formed to support education about different diseases.   Try to obtain enough information that you can see pictures in your mind about what is actually happening to the body parts or systems involved. These pictures can then be the basis of scenes in which healing actions created by you, are taking place.

Step 11

Most importantly, do not let a healthcare provider give you a death sentence. When they say that with this certain condition, your life expectancy is so many months or years, they are speaking of tendencies or of averages only, without considering you as a bio-chemically and spiritually diverse individual.

I have a dear friend whose M.D. gave him three years to live because he had tested HIV+ with the AIDS virus. My friend replied "Who knows, I may be going to your funeral?" Four years later, having stopped smoking and drinking, and after receiving Reiki, chiropractic, and anthropsophical homeopathics, he is incredibly healthy. He bought his first home two years ago and is presently negotiating the purchase of a restaurant. His heart has opened to himself and to receiving the love and support of his friends.

Today, he is happier and more serene than I have ever known him to be.

Remember, if you are reading this book, you have more interest, more knowledge, and more power for self-healing than the people in the statistical pool to whom you are being compared.

There are certainly a great many *cures* that take place without self-love or love from one's family or practitioner. But to truly awaken the healer within and unleash that wonderful power, love is one of the very necessary ingredients. The other valuable keys are faith, or a complete paradigm shift.

Deepak Chopra tells a story well worth repeating. A female patient who was complaining of abdominal pain and jaundice was sent for gallbladder surgery, but when the surgeons found cancer throughout her abdomen, they considered it inoperable and closed her back up. The patient's daughter pleaded with Chopra not to tell her mother the truth, so he told her the gall stones had been successfully removed and assumed she had only a few months to live. Eight months later, the woman returned to him for a routine physical exam, and had no symptoms or signs of cancer. A year later, she told him, "Doctor, I was so sure I had cancer that when it turned out to be just gallstones, I told myself I would never be sick another day in my life." He says her cancer never recurred. This woman certainly awakened her inner healer in a most profound way.

Awakening Your Healing Abilities Towards Others

Family, friends, and co-workers all want to help the injured or ill patient and need not feel helpless. Their love will be positive energy which *pluses* the patient's self-love or fills in if the patient has not yet been able to enact self-love. The love of others may be critical if the patient's self-love is low or they are unconscious and unable to use it. Prayer is a wonderful manifestation of this love.

Another helpful way to use your healing ability for the benefit of others is to picture them as healthy in mind, body, and spirit. Don't focus on their outwardly disabled body, and don't treat a disfigured person as though their mind were disfigured also. When we stay in touch with others, mind to mind, or body to body, our healing energy flows easily.

The most important lesson to be remembered is that when people are in pain of any sort, what they want most is to be loved, reassured, touched, held, and told that they will not be abandoned.

There are times when the illness represents a cry from the body or the mind for help/healing of all the old wounds that got them to this point. Ram Dass says it so eloquently when he reminds us to give "heart-to-heart resuscitation".

As lay healers for others, it is good to remember the power of words. There's the old story about a group of workers deciding to pull a prank on their new co-worker. All during the morning, several of them would tell him how terrible he looked, and ask if he was sick? At first, he replied "No, I feel just fine." But by noon, he indeed looked and felt ill and had to leave for home. When someone is already in ill health, their mind puts greater weight on the horror stories related to them about someone with the same condition. It is not worth mentioning at all unless the story is certain to empower and encourage them.

Just as we all have capabilities as healers, we are all capable of experiencing and expressing love. Love may be something that doesn't come naturally to us, but that we consciously decide to learn, to the enormous benefit of ourselves and those we want to assist in healing. As my eight-year old daughter, Jessie says, "Love is something to share with everyone."

Touching is one of the ways we can be most useful as lay healers. Just as touching is necessary for the survival of the newborn, it is enormously important for the ill or injured person. Many elderly patients seek medical advice primarily out of the need to be touched.

Try to remember back to when you were little and how comforting and healing it was to be held if you were sick, sad, or hurt. Often when, as adults, we are sick, sad, or hurt, it is as though we were little again; we feel weak or unempowered, and being hugged, held or touched can be reassuring, energizing, and healing.

Touching is like any other healing skill and can be learned. The more we use the skill, the better it becomes. It is as though we were learning to play the piano or read Braille. By using the hands and fingers for loving touch, the nerve pathways get used repeatedly and become highly developed. My patients always ask me how I can tell where all the sore spots are and I reply that the tissue texture is so different at the pain areas that they literally jump out at my fingers.

Touching did not come naturally; I grew up in a family in which there wasn't a lot of touching and I never felt very comfortable doing it. I was in my mid-twenties and attending parties given by two lovely Polish women (who are still generators of love) who were able to touch all of their friends in the warmest, most affectionate and non-sexual way. And as I watched them, I kept thinking, "Oh, that looks so good, I would love to be able to do that!" I started to emulate them more and more, reaching and touching people's arms or their hands, and it got easier and easier. By the time I'd made my decision to become a chiropractor, I realized I was definitely going to learn to touch people.

Now, not only does it feel natural and easy, but it is also something I would miss profoundly were not I allowed to do it. I love to flow energy to people through my hands and through my body when I am hugging. I have a lot of love to give, and touching is a joyfully wonderful way to share it.

Awaken Your Healers' Abilities To Heal

This section is intended to help patients and their loved ones to understand what qualities to look for in a healer. It is also to help them realize that healers are people with needs of their own, regardless of how highly-trained they are. It should also prove useful for anyone considering the healing arts as a profession and for those already practising the healing arts, who desire to give even better healing service and care.

There are many ways to become a health care professional. Most people follow an academic route in the beginning until they begin to feel comfortable developing their natural ability. Love is probably the greatest key in transforming a trained professional into a healer. It is the element which allows us to reach into ourselves and recognize that we all have healing powers. Love, as in any other area of our life, fosters expansion and growth, so that the healing talent becomes more and more useful.

The Four Elements Of Healing

Physical

The physical element consists of knowledge, and training in procedures. It is the technique used on the physical body, whether that be surgery, drugs, manipulation, massage, laying on of hands, herbs, dances, etc.. This myriad of techniques allows the healer a variety of expressions. All of them have benefit and get results, because more than any other group, healers demand good results for their patients.

If there was one technique that worked all the time for all patients, I can almost guarantee that we would all be using it. But part of the beauty of life is the diversity within the sameness, and thus God has allowed there to be a multitude of avenues through which the body will accept healing to take place. Each person has a biochemical, physical, emotional, and mental make-up that make them truly individual. Thus, it is both the patient's and the healer's responsibility to explore various techniques until the right combination is found.

Mental

The mental element of healing includes the projected thought in the healer's mind of the patient's response and outcome. Positive expectation on the healer's part is extremely important. And the wise healer recognizes the truth of Norman Cousin's statement in the book *Healers on Healing*, "The patient's hopes are the physician's best ally."

As the intention of the healer becomes directed towards a positive healing experience for the patient, the healer's verbal and non-verbal communication will convey a sense of confidence to the patient that activates their own self-healing abilities. The non-verbal communication of attitudes, beliefs, and emotions is a dynamic force in giving compassion, empathy, and love.

Verbal communication should include, in words that create simple pictures in the patient's mind, a simple explanation of their condition, of the healthy function of the organs involved, and how that healthy function has varied in the diseased state. Enough information should be given that the patient's fear, confusion, and sense of mystery can be diminished and they can create their own pictures of healing with scenes played out to the desired conclusion. A healer's training has given them knowledge and expertise that patients need in order to dispel their fear. Sometimes, verbal communication includes what is obvious to the healer but not to the patient, like telling them that they need to go home and rest.

Whatever else the verbal communication includes, don't let it be a death sentence. Don't rob the patient of their hope by telling them it's in their head or there's nothing wrong with them. If they are not responding to your treatment, and you have no further therapy to offer, refer them to someone with a different technique or approach.

If a patient has been referred to me by a massage therapist and isn't responding to chiropractic as expected, I usually order an MRI and refer to a neurologist or orthopedist. If they've had all the sophisticated examinations and haven't responded to the therapy of an M.D., and I'm not getting good enough results, I may refer them to a massage therapist or acupuncturist.

Intuition

The third element of healing is intuition. With all the training and education in place and all the specific information a healer has gathered about the patient—through the history, examination and observation placed into that wonderful computer we call our mind—we add the store of experience from treating other patients. Then, instead of using rote formulas which dismiss the individual diversity of the patient, it is time to let intuition personalize the treatment. Albert Schweitzer stated this principle eloquently when he said, "Medicine is not only a science, but also the art of letting our own individuality interact with the individuality of the patient."

There can be great fun and joy in exercising the intuitive faculty in healing. It is extremely easy to be overly serious because it is the patient's health with which you are concerned, but it can hasten creative solutions to occasionally imagine yourself as a super sleuth, resolving a complex mystery. Do you need more clues, or should you go back and reinvestigate some information that doesn't quite fit the way it should?

Emotional

The last element is the emotional part. This involves the expression by the healer of pure, unconditional love, without judgment, which unites the healer with the spiritual energy of divine and universal intelligence and allows the patient's innate intelligence to flourish.

It is important to remember that the practitioner is a *vehicle* for healing, not the healing itself. Although we train our minds, our hands, and even our hearts, in the end, we need to keep all that training available and then let go and become an open conduit for universal intelligence to flow into, through, and out of us to the patient.

Practising healing on this emotional, spiritual level brings the healer into a very blessed position. To be able to place your hands on a patient and sense the trust and positive expectancy of help and healing is a tremendous honor and privilege.

The Essential Ingredient

Self-love is an invaluable quality that all practitioners should strive for, be they neurosurgeons, family practitioners, chiropractors or massage therapists. Their effectiveness in the daily practice of their specialities will be a reflection of three characteristics. One will be their ability to focus on the patient and the necessary procedure. One will be how well they've learned to manage their Type A personality. And the other will be the amount and quality of self-love they have developed.

The healing professions attract dedicated and hard-working individuals. The training is arduous and demands a large amount of sacrifice. Also, the types of people drawn to the healing professions are usually those who are very self-sacrificing and who have a deep desire to serve their fellow humans.

I think for most of us, it is only later that we realize that our strong attraction to the healing profession was often due to a need to heal ourselves through the knowledge learned and through the experience of service. Practising is indeed a continuing exploration towards improvement. On this physical plane of existence, we aren't perfect, and we must accept this about ourselves. It is our responsibility to give our very best, coming from a position of full integrity and love, and then allow the patient to do with that as they will. We must learn to let go of the failures and move on to those patients we can better help.

Because of the seriousness of what healing practitioners do, it is important we keep our humanity intact and remain open, whether that means allowing our patients to call us by our first name, if they like, or by hugging a patient when it's what they need and would be appropriately received. Occasionally, we open ourselves too much and begin to experience the patient's symptoms when we overstep empathy into self-sacrifice. Experiencing a patient's symptoms definitely increases our compassion level and may be very enlightening in determining how we will treat that condition in the future. But I believe we should strive to keep our bodies and minds healthy. A healer's compassion level will remain high if they keep in mind that most patients have virtually no idea as to what is happening to them and that they are extremely afraid and often in pain.

Another important aspect of self-love as a practitioner is learning the art of saying no when it's necessary. Healers know intuitively when what they're doing is of benefit to the patient and when their attention is somewhere else completely and they're performing true malpractice. Our responsibility is to either bring our focus back to the patient or physically remove ourselves from the healer's role. This can be temporary, as in an infectious illness when we aren't at our mental best, or if, in more pervasive situations, we need time off to take care of ourselves. It may be time to take a vacation, bring in a substitute for a while, hire a partner and work fewer hours, or change jobs.

One of my spiritual teachers, Leland Val Van de Wall, who travels 40 weeks a year giving seminars, was once asked where he most liked to be and he replied "Where I am now". That is what we should strive for in both our professional and our private lives, to mentally be with the patient when we are physically with them, and conversely, to be with our family, friends, and our own creative minds when we are away from the office.

As our level of self-love grows, we are better able to suspend judgement regarding the patient's illness or condition. We should also learn to suspend judgement around what the patient chooses to do with the healing techniques we provide. We may decide to disentangle ourselves from a patient who refuses to follow any of our directives and advice, and that is all right. However, we must not abandon the patient who continues to want our services but is not yet able to heal as quickly or fully as are other patients.

It is our responsibility to deliver the very best treatment of which we are capable and then let go of the situation. The patient will do with it what they are able or willing to do. Both patient and healer have their own areas of responsibility in the healing process. The patient's expectations may be very different from those of the practitioner. They may have reached a level which we would find unacceptable but that is more than satisfactory for them.

Loving The Healer Within Precedes Results

I think of the many successful results of patients I have treated over the years. I have an immense satisfaction in seeing them return with an expanded appreciation of the normal activities that they enjoyed before their injury or acute condition. They also enjoy being able to do new things, having better energy, more self-love and a new found wholeness of health through chiropractic.

Another special joy for myself and my staff is to watch the unfolding of people who come to the office full of pain and fear, closed down upon themselves, short-tempered and gruff in their interactions with us. Within a few short weeks, we find out who they really are. We see by their actions—their kindness, their interest in others, their sharing of enjoyment of their families—that they are fulfilling more of their human potential through healing.

W. LAWRENCE CLAPP

In a business renowned for its adversarial relationships, it is refreshing to find a real estate developer who is not only respected, but one who is held in such high esteem to be asked to chair several important committees. W. Lawrence (Larry) Clapp is just such a developer and individual. He is a graduate of the University of Michigan with a Bachelor of Arts degree, and completed his post-graduate work with a J.D. degree from the University of Michigan Law School in 1963.

Prior to launching his civilian career, Mr. Clapp was a Lieutenant in the U.S. Navy from 1956 to 1961, serving as senior aide to Admiral Williamson.

Following completion of his law degree, Lawrence was a practicing attorney in Honolulu, with emphasis on litigation, trust, tax, real estate, and development. From 1967 to 1990, Mr. Clapp was the President and CEO of the Trousdale Murchison Companies, a multi-million dollar development and construction firm in Hawaii and California.

During his tenure at the Trousdale Murchison Companies, he also served on various Executive Committees and was Director of the Hawaii Bar Association, the Young President's Organization Hawaii Chapter, the Chamber of Commerce of Hawaii, the Bank of Honolulu, and the Hawaii Opera Theater.

Lawrence Clapp has always taken an active interest in his community and has been chair or director of numerous public and private authorities, schools, committees, associations, and foundations. He currently chairs the Honolulu Transit Authority.

He is the President and CEO of Environmental Developers Inc., with offices in Oakland, California and Honolulu, Hawaii, and may be contacted by writing to 760 Longridge Road, Oakland, CA, 94610, or by telephoning (510) 836-1155.

5 | A PERSONAL HEALING

You Can Heal Yourself; Anyone Can!

With abundant help from the universe, I have seen my life transformed in approximately four years, from one of suicidal pain, misery, and economic hardship to one of purpose, joy, and abundance. Life has become fun and wondrously magical all day, every day.

By looking within and tuning into the universe, all manner of human ailments can be healed. Whatever ailments we create, including emotional pain, physical pain, and economic hardships, are learning tools for our growth. When we can learn the lessons and move on, we become healed.

This does not mean that life is without problems. Rather, it means that problems have become fewer and smaller as a result of viewing them as lessons instead of disasters. By trusting in self and the universe, I find solutions previously unseen appearing seemingly out of nowhere, and all in perfect timing. I must emphasize again that problems are only opportunities for our own learning, that when we believe and trust in the universe, magical solutions happen!

Life is such that if we can get the message from small problems and ailments, we don't need to experience the larger, catastrophic problems and illnesses in order to learn. If we begin to listen to the messages or the whispers, the problems soon become smaller— life begins to flow easier and becomes more enjoyable.

By sharing my experiences in healing physical ailments, from prostate cancer, scoliosis, constant suicidal migraines, sinus problems "requiring surgery", to emotional, relationship, and economic problems, I hope to show you how you can permanently change your life. I would like to inspire you to begin immediately! By merely making the decision to do so, you will begin the process. You can get help from an abundance of sources whenever you need it. It is readily available. The universe wants your healing as much as you do and will do everything to facilitate it if you will make the decision, be willing, and do the work of looking within. My life is living proof that it works.

Success Is Not Enough

By the age of 40, I had reached a level of success envied by many.   I had graduated from law practice, achieved a multi-million dollar net worth, was President of a major corporation, owner of a captained seagoing yacht, chairman of many groups and organizations, including the Young Presidents Organization in Hawaii, and was on the cover of Hawaii Business Magazine as Business Man of the Year.   Highly involved in community affairs, I was often interviewed on television and was advisor to many, yet I was finding that this did not bring happiness. I began to ask myself if there was more to life than material success and recognition in one's community.

This inquiry process lasted several years. During this time, I sought answers in various religions, para-normal healing, numerous business/personal seminars, and ultimately found answers in metaphysical principles. These principles are now discussed in the media and are espoused by national, best-selling authors such as Anthony Robbins, Deepak Chopra, Wayne Dyer and Shirley MacLaine. These are timeless principles of our universe which predate and were the original foundation of all organized religions.

Material, physical attainment is not the measure of true success. Real success and happiness in life comes from the inner understanding, that we do indeed create our own reality and living the responsibility that entails. Real growth must follow and is accelerated by a deeper knowing and loving ourselves, especially as we can help others in their growth. Success and happiness is achieved by the person who understands, at the emotional level, and lives, that we truly do create our own reality.

Growth Choice

Having begun my inquiry whether there must be more than material business and community success, I sought the answers from a variety of sources. One was to go back to nature. I bought 40 acres of virgin land and became a banana farmer in Hawaii. This enabled me to begin to be in touch with nature and the universe, but I still did not see how it could all work in my life. Rather than getting better, as I had anticipated, things were getting worse.

As I understand the process now, the whispers were becoming shouts until I was forced to pay attention. I began to have worse migraines on a much more frequent basis, and my problems in business became monumental.   My relationships were not what I wanted, and my life seemed to be going downhill. It got worse through a business bankruptcy, and migraines so excruciating that all I sought was a way out. On two occasions, I actually loaded the gun. Something always kept me from pulling the trigger, for which I am now very thankful to my higher self!

The pain ultimately forced me to seek alternative sources of healing.   I needed help– and I needed it immediately. A business associate mentioned her success with a rolfer. I sought him out and began learning through the deep tissue work, what unreleased anger and other emotions had done to my body. I began to make conscious choices instead of just reacting, and to take some responsibility for what was happening in my life. I began to see what it could feel like to be free of pain, even for short periods of time.

Rolfing thus helped me get back in touch with my body and my inner being. This led to more specific inquiry, ultimately finding answers in the workshops, tapes, and books of Lazaris who teaches regularly in various cities across the United States.

Lazaris provided the direction and guidance to make my growth choice become a reality in my life.

The Healing Begins

Having made a decision for growth and for healing, the healing could begin. Rolfing happened to be my first introduction to taking responsibility for my own body and beginning to change old beliefs. Chiropractic, rebirthing, massage, and other disciplines also helped.

Through conditioning, we are taught that others do it to us, whether it's loved ones, doctors, enemies, God, or the world. We are not taught to take responsibility for ourselves, nor that we do create our entire reality. As Lazaris says so often, there are no asterisks, no footnotes, no exceptions; we do create every bit of our own reality. This is wonderful because it gives us the power to change it!

As Dr. Wayne Dyer says so well, "You'll see it when you believe it." Our beliefs are the very root and basis of our entire physical and emotional reality. So when we believe that life is a struggle, life will be a struggle. If we believe in pain, we will have pain. It is necessary to change these beliefs and to take responsibility for our own body and our own reality in order to begin to heal.

To get our attention, our higher selves give us ever more poignant messages such as illnesses, problems, or other issues. When we can receive these messages quickly and easily, we don't have to have a bigger lesson or message. For example, if I am doing something and it doesn't work out properly, I need to look at the message behind why it isn't working out properly. Maybe it isn't the thing that I should be doing right now, or maybe there is an easier way. So, I will ask the universe for help or for a vision of a clearer way to proceed. The help is always there when I am open to receive it!

Healing our emotions and our physical body depends on our belief that we are responsible and in charge. If we expect the doctor, or a pill, or somebody to do it for us, it may or may not work. Even when it does work, another lesson will come until we learn. Ultimately, taking responsibility, listening to the whispers or messages, and taking appropriate action will produce the healing. God and the universe do not create our illness—we do, our very own selves. We have the power to change, by getting the message of the illness, whether it is to rest, or to recognize and release some anger or other stored "stuff". If we will get the message and visualize the ailment healed, it will soon be healed. As I could understand these basic metaphysical principles (many of which I learned from a Lazaris tape entitled *Healing; The Nature of Health, Parts 1 and 2*), my ailments began to heal. I became a happier person surrounded by nicer people, and good things started happening in my life. The ailments that I had had for many, many years—some for a lifetime—began to disappear as the healer within awakened.

Revelations - Taking Responsibility

As I began to see and live the principle that I truly did create my own reality, my life began to change in miraculous ways. I could consistently create parking places, favorable results in meetings, new business ventures, and projects when by all "normal" standards, the money wasn't there and it shouldn't have been possible. In other words, miracles began happening in my life with considerable regularity, simply by taking responsibility and looking within during daily meditations. The people in my life also began to change. I began to attract nicer, more fun-loving people, and the victims and more difficult people began to drift out of my life.

An early example occurred as I visualized a new business partnership. Without knowing what that would be, I received a phone call "out of the blue" from my accountant indicating that another client of his wanted to go into partnership with me. This business proved to be fun and profitable, quite unlike the ones I used to create.

I began to understand that each of us is a consciousness that has had many lives before and may yet have many hereafter. We are temporarily occupying our body on this planet for the purpose of learning. As Lazaris says, we have come here for two purposes: 1) to learn to consciously create our reality; 2) to learn to have fun doing it. When we leave this planet and return to the spirit world, there will be no time and no boundaries. Our thoughts will manifest instantly. It is therefore important that we learn to manifest our reality consciously and to have only those thoughts that we wish to create. On this planet, we have the luxury of time to enable us to learn the creating process. Can you imagine if our thoughts manifested instantly, as in other dimensions? Most of us would create some pretty undesirable results!

Within months of learning to take responsibility and to change old beliefs, I was making far more profits than ever before in my life and was creating wonderful things. Among others, I created a beautiful six-bedroom, 10,500 square foot home for my family when I had neither the money nor any right to believe that I could create such a fabulous home. Thus, taking responsibility and changing old beliefs are the first important steps to awaken the healer within.

Getting Help

There is a metaphysical saying that when the student is ready, the teacher will appear. I have found this to be absolutely true. As we are ready and willing, teachers appear in the most wondrous ways. For example, one night, after seeing a movie next door, I was drawn to step into a metaphysical bookstore. I had just been reading the Louise Hay book *How To Love Yourself* and wishing I had some direct help, as I was having difficulty with how and whether it was proper or appropriate for me to love myself. A flyer and a poster just inside the bookstore announced a local seminar by Louise Hay the coming week-end entitled *How To Love Yourself!* I was able to sign up for the workshop and receive great benefit at that time; just right for what I was working on. I also met others in the seminar who have been most helpful to me since that time, most notably Dr. Pratiba Eastwood, a spiritual metaphysical counselor in Honolulu.

Other teachers who have appeared magically at just the right time for me have been spiritual beings channeled by various people. Their advice has always been loving and right on. They have helped me through some very difficult periods in my life and some continue to advise me on fun and high growth projects.

As we become more centered and more focused, it is quite easy to communicate with the universe while relaxing in meditation, driving down the road, or walking in the woods. The universe has a fun and wondrous way of communicating with us and putting helpful ideas in our head at the most appropriate times. Help is always available when we ask. Even doing small jobs, I have found that any time I ask the universe for help, it is always there. It never fails. The most frustrating projects get done quickly and magically. Try it, you will be amazed!

When you are ready, the teacher will appear. You only need to be open, willing, and do a little seeking.

Creating What We Want

Most of us have already experienced wanting something with real emotional clarity and had it manifest elegantly. When we are truly centered and clear about what it is we want, we will manifest it unless we have hidden agendas such as fear, doubt, anger, or other unreleased emotions. Such blockages prevent our manifesting the desired result. But, with truth and clarity, we can all create miracles!

To create something, we must first make a decision that we really do want to create it. Secondly, it helps to write down what it is we want, why we want it, why we won't let ourselves have it, and why we doubt that we will get it. Thirdly, process and release these blockages such as fear, anger, dishonesty, or lack of deservability. Fourthly, it is important to put clear thoughts, emotions, and visualizations out into the universe, so that the universe is clear on just what it is we want to manifest. When we are clear, some indication of the manifestation will appear within 72 hours. If not, reprocess and reprogram. It works!

After processing the blockages, there are many techniques to visualize what it is we want. The one that has worked best for me is one from

Lazaris called *The 33-Second Technique*. In this technique, you visualize, in meditation, a symbol or tabloid of what it is you want and the emotions that you see yourself in when you get it, for exactly 33 seconds. (A good, inexpensive second timer is available from Radio Shack.) For example, you might visualize how happy you are upon receiving that check; or how ecstatic you are driving that new car; or how proudly you are crossing the threshold of that new home. The vision should be simple so that it is easy to remember and repeated without change, several times during the day, or at least, daily until it is realized. The visualization should incorporate all five senses: smell, taste, touch, sound, and sight.

If, after days of visualization, the subject is not created, then it is time to reprocess and to look for blockages of why you are not willing to receive. The blockages are usually easy to find and can then be released. Repeat the programming technique and continue until it is created.

There are many other techniques that can be used, but *The 33-Second Technique* is the easiest and the most successful. I have created new businesses plus a new home for my family, and have healed many things utilizing this technique.

Perhaps the example most worth repeating here was in March of 1989 when I began to visualize a fabulous new home for my family. Things began falling into place very quickly. The property of our dreams, which the church had said they would never sell, suddenly became available to us. A world-class architect appeared with just the plan we wanted, the bank readily agreed to finance the home, and just the right contractors appeared.

On July 22, we demolished the old building, and on December 15, in time for Christmas of the same year, we moved into our new 6-bedroom home with over 10,500 sq. ft. of living space, with beautifully landscaped and secure grounds. By most standards, it could not be done, but the luxury home was built in 4 1/2 months.

You, too, can create whatever you want in life following simple, metaphysical principles.

Releasing The Past

Focusing on the past and comparing today with yesterday locks us in the failures and problems of yesterday. There is a great metaphysical saying that where the attention goes, the energy flows. Where the energy flows is what we create. Thus, if we focus on the past, we perpetuate it.

We perpetuate the problems that we seek to eliminate.

A helpful technique to release the past, is to spend a few moments to go back over one's life and to construct a time line on a piece of paper. A time line is simply the highlighting of the major emotional events, happy and unhappy, of one's lifetime. A time line can be simply a long line with approximate ages under the line and events on top of the line, in cryptic handwriting. (It is only for you, so don't get caught up in trying to do it perfectly!) Examples of events are different for each of us, but some typical ones are: abuse of any kind; birth of a sibling and attendant loss of attention, or abandonment; punishment that created anger, an "I don't deserve" feeling, or shame. Show all major events on through school to the present. Look in particular for that inevitable, deep wounding, such as loss of a first love or loss of a loved one during the teenage years.

Then, go back over these events quietly in meditation, feeling the feelings that weren't felt or weren't released at the time, and feel them deeply with tears, yelling, hitting, or whatever feels right until they are dissipated in meditation. It may take a few minutes or it may take hours. Repeat if necessary. Stick with it! You will know when it is done. Once these feelings are released from your body and your being, you can go forward with a clearer and happier vision of your reality.

It is absolutely essential to release the past. Many of us feel we are unhappy because of something that our mother or father or an ex-spouse has done to us, and we continue to blame our unhappiness on them. The fact is that whoever it was and however terrible it may have been, they are not doing it to us now; we are doing it to ourselves on a current basis. It is absolutely essential to take responsibility, to release the past, and to forgive the persons involved, including ourselves, in order to move forward. Then our visions of the future can create the wondrous reality of our dreams.

Freedom

Freedom is our ultimate goal, freedom to make choices. Choices are freedom. When we are controlled by our vision of what somebody else wants us to be, in the form of trying to be perfect, or to please a loved one, or to cover up the persona that we see as that awful person inside us, we cannot have freedom.

Freedom is realizing who we are, loving ourselves for who we are now, and making choices that help us to know ourselves better and to love ourselves better.

Things that we are doing out of obligation need to be re-evaluated and either dropped, or be acknowledged to be things that we do because we want to do them. Obligations are not freedom. Doing something to please mother, who may be long gone, or father, ex-spouses, teachers, or whoever is not freedom. Freedom allows us to follow our own intuition, which is variably called divine guidance or flowing with the universe.

Following our every intuition brings true happiness which, put another way, is the ability to flow with the universe and to receive the joyous and wondrous things the universe offers us. These cannot be experienced while living life out of obligation or seeking validation from others. True self-love and self-esteem come only from within through maximizing our personal freedom and following our every intuition.

Being free of obligation applies to one's work, hobbies, visits with friends and relatives—to everything we do. We need to re-evaluate our doings.   If we are not doing what makes us happy, then we need to change it. Either change our perception or change what we are doing, because as long as we are doing out of obligation, we cannot be happy.

Abundance

In my experience, when I am making choices that make me free and happy (in other words, doing what I truly love, particularly if it is helping others to grow), I create an abundance economically and in every other aspect of my life. There is no scarcity in the world; the scarcity exists only in our perception. If we believe in security and lack, then security and lack will be our reality. When we can truly see that the universe provides everything if we love and trust in it, then abundance will flow in our lives.

I strongly recommend the authoritative work on abundance: *Creating Money* by Sanaya Roman and Duane Packer.

Healing The Body

During the past three years, I have healed myself of prostate cancer, debilitating arthritis of the neck, suicidal migraine headaches, and a sinus condition requiring surgery, plus numerous lesser ailments.

My prostate cancer was discovered by PSA and biopsy in December, and by March, the healing began to be evidenced by an improved PSA . The PSA went from a high of 7.2 down to below normal of 2.6 and has stayed that way now for over a year.

Doctors, and chiropractors, used to put 20 years of X-rays of my neck on the wall and show me the growth of the arthritis in my neck until it appeared as a solid mass over and between four vertebrae. The only way I could look behind was to turn my whole body and shoulders because my neck wouldn't move any more.   As I released the past, with its anger and other stuffed emotions, while visualizing my neck improving, with the help of chiropractic, I slowly regained motion. My neck is now clear of any arthritis on X-rays, moves freely, nearly painlessly, and continues to improve.

The sinus condition for which I was strongly urged to have surgery also has cleared up. The migraines are now reduced to very seldom, and are no longer debilitating. Relationships have healed and I find that I attract a much more fun, honest, and wondrous type of people into my life.

These healings occurred quite easily when I learned to feel and release my emotions on a current basis as well as go back and release past, stuffed emotions. When we live in freedom and happiness and make choices which accentuate our freedom and happiness, we can heal ailments with ease and soon begin to have fewer of them.

My specific healings were assisted greatly by the Lazaris tapes on the *Healing; The Nature of Health*. Essentially, all healing is frequent and regular visualization of the ailment already healed while visualizing the universe pumping energy and light into that portion of the body to facilitate the healing. The visualization can also be of ourself doing what it is the injury or ailment currently prevents us from doing, happily and joyously, while asking the universe for help. Do this on a daily basis and you will be amazed at the results.

Naturally, the extent to which we live healthy lives, eating healthily, without alcohol, tobacco and other addictions assists our bodily healing. It is difficult to heal specific ailments while lowering our bodily energies with addictive substances. These need to be dropped and *can be dropped* by applying metaphysical principles previously discussed, and/or by getting help from the many sources available. You can heal yourself by awakening the healer within.

Epilogue

My three-year healing has not been without doubts and "I can'ts", especially in the beginning. Frustration and doubt soon gave way to fun and wonder in small ways. I have progressed from a suicidally unhappy person in constant economic trouble to a person nearly free of pain and problems, creating lots of fun and magic in my life every day. I am filled with joyous gratitude for the help that teachers, healers, God, and the universe have provided to me.

I am now using my experience to help others (hopefully including you, the reader) which gives me even greater happiness and enjoyment. I also find that my life becomes far simpler and much more peaceful, which like a *Catch 22* in reverse, greatly speeds my growth!

Wherever you may be in your growth, please begin to expand your own growth and healing, now, this very minute! To begin only requires a decision to do so. **The only time we have is NOW!** All change occurs Now!

Helpful Books / Resources

Chopra M.D., Deepak.
Quantum Healing

Concept Synergy (800) 628-2356
Lazaris Books, Tapes, and Seminars

Dyer, Dr. Wayne.
When You Believe It, You See It

Hay, Louise.
Heal Your Body

Hay, Louise.
Love Yourself, Heal Your Life

MacLaine, Shirley.
Going Within

Roman, Sanaya and Packer Ph.D., Duane.
Creating Money

Roman, Sanaya.
Books I, II, & III of the Earth Life Series
Living With Joy: Keys to Personal Power and Spiritual Transformation
Personal Power Through Awareness: A Guidebook for Sensitive People
Spiritual Growth: Being Your Higher Self

Roman, Sanaya and Packer Ph.D., Duane.
Opening to Channel: How to Connect with Your Guide